D1645098

2016

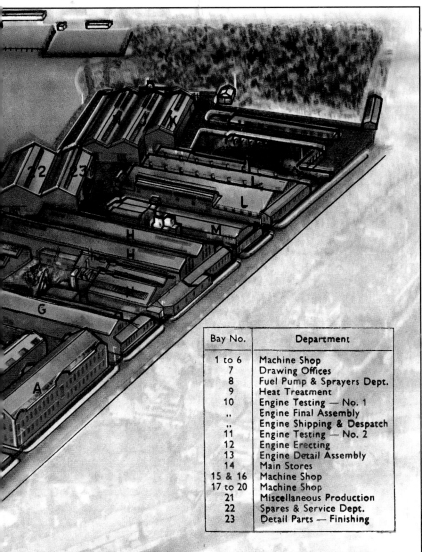

Bay No.	Department
1 to 6	Machine Shop
7	Drawing Offices
8	Fuel Pump & Sprayers Dept.
9	Heat Treatment
10	Engine Testing — No. 1
,,	Engine Final Assembly
,,	Engine Shipping & Despatch
11	Engine Testing — No. 2
12	Engine Erecting
13	Engine Detail Assembly
14	Main Stores
15 & 16	Machine Shop
17 to 20	Machine Shop
21	Miscellaneous Production
22	Spares & Service Dept.
23	Detail Parts — Finishing

HALL ENGINE WORKS

GARDNER ARE MADE.

DIESEL ENGINES

NGINES (SALES) LTD.

ORRIS, HENTY & GARDNERS, LTD.

etors : L. Gardner & Sons, Ltd.)

WORKS, PATRICROFT, MANCHESTER.

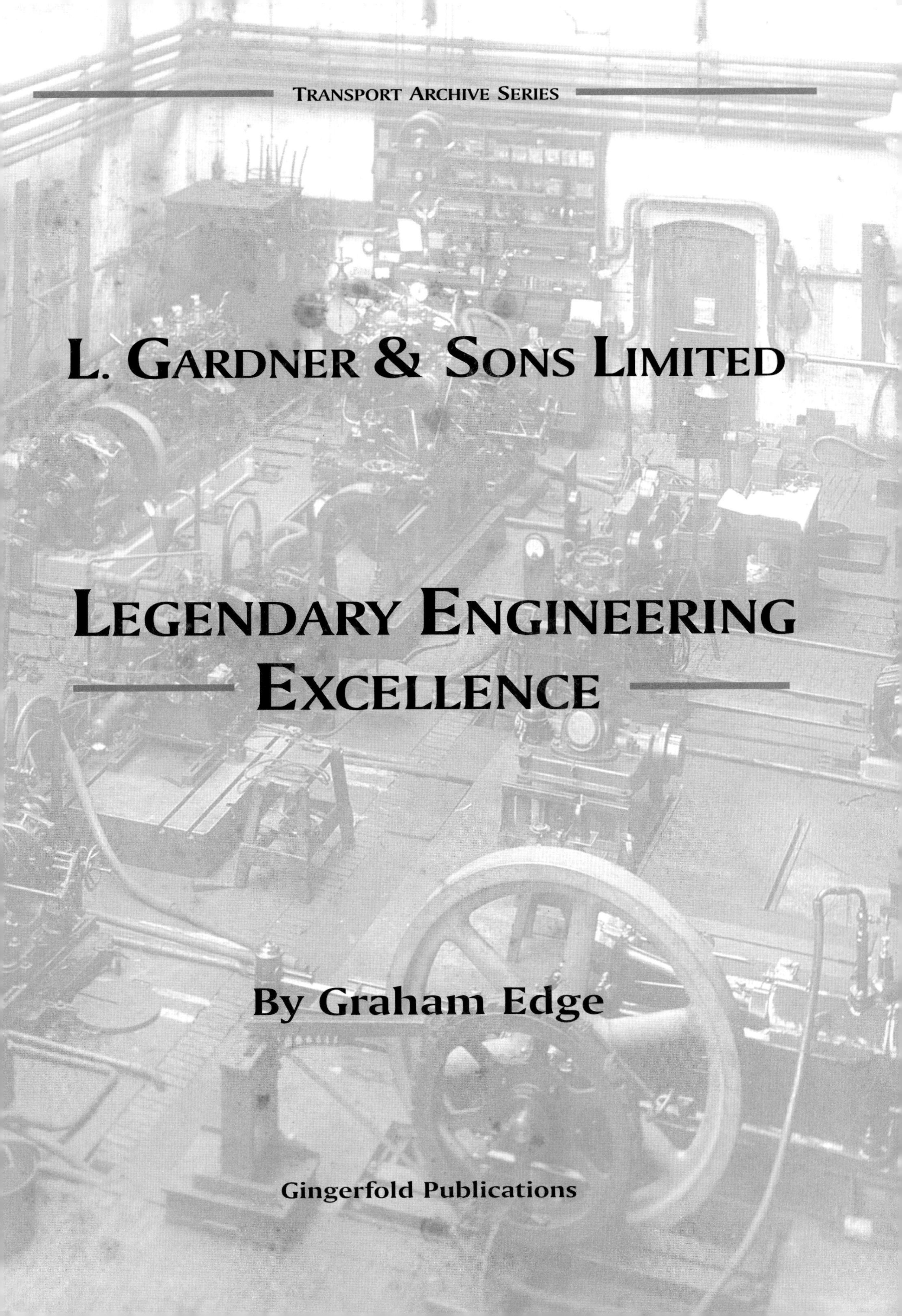

TRANSPORT ARCHIVE SERIES

L. GARDNER & SONS LIMITED

LEGENDARY ENGINEERING EXCELLENCE

By Graham Edge

Gingerfold Publications

THIS BOOK IS DEDICATED TO
ALL THOSE WHO STRIVE FOR PERFECTION
AND ACHIEVE EXCELLENCE IN THEIR CHOSEN FIELDS

ACKNOWLEDGEMENTS

Without the input of Dion Houghton into this project it would never have happened. For over six years Dion, the former Sales Director of L. Gardner & Sons Limited, has made his comprehensive knowledge of the company freely available to me. He has opened up his vast archive of material and photographs and read, corrected, and suggested alterations to several drafts of this text. Dion's father, Gordon Houghton was a Director of Norris, Henty, & Gardners in 1926, so Dion has an unsurpassed insight into the company dating to those pioneering times when automotive diesel engines cemented Gardner's reputation for premium quality. This book is as much Dion Houghton's as it is mine.

If Dion Houghton provided information from his perspective of a long serving, senior employee and Director, then what better person could also provide details of his family's company than Paul Gardner, the great-grandson of the founder? Paul worked for the firm for much of his working life and still runs a successful Gardner engine remanufacturing company. Paul read the final draft and suggested several important amendments. He also consented to write a foreword to this book.

To Dion Houghton and Paul Gardner I record my grateful thanks. If they are satisfied with the veracity and accuracy of this work, then so am I.

PHOTOGRAPHIC CREDITS

The majority of photographs reproduced in this book are from the collections of Dion Houghton and Paul Gardner, and are official L. Gardner and Sons Limited material. Where the original photographer is known it has been credited in the caption, and if there was any doubt as to the origin of a photograph, then every effort has been made to trace the copyright holder. Other photograph sources have also been acknowledged in the caption.

The Transport Archive Series is produced and published by Gingerfold Publications.
This title was first published in November 2002 by Gingerfold Publications,
8, Tothill Road, Swaffham Prior, Cambridge, CB5 0JX.

COPYRIGHT: Graham Edge and Gingerfold Publications. All rights reserved.

ISBN 1-902356-10-1

Book design by Tina Ranft, Yew Design, Melbourn, Royston, Herts. SG8 6EP.
Printed by The Burlington Press, Foxton, Cambridge, CB2 6SW

CONTENTS

FOREWORD: Page 4

INTRODUCTION: Page 5

CHAPTER 1: FOUNDING A FAMILY DYNASTY   Page 6

CHAPTER 2: SHAPING THE FIRM'S FUTURE   Page 9

CHAPTER 3: A NEW FACTORY FOR A NEW CENTURY   Page 17

CHAPTER 4: TROUBLED TIMES   Page 50

CHAPTER 5: REVOLUTIONISING ROAD TRANSPORT   Page 66

CHAPTER 6: MEETING UNPRECEDENTED DEMANDS   Page 93

CHAPTER 7: THE HEYDAY OF GARDNER ENGINES   Page 121

CHAPTER 8: A CENTENARY IN A TIME OF CHANGE   Page 158

CHAPTER 9: END OF AN ERA   Page 176

CHAPTER 10: NEW ENGINE DESIGNS   Page 188

CHAPTER 11: IN CONCLUSION and EPILOGUE   Page 195

APPENDICES   Pages 199–206

INDEX   Page 207

FOREWORD

This is without doubt the most complete and detailed work on L. Gardner & Sons Limited, its personnel and its products, from formation to effective collapse. The author, Graham Edge and the historian behind it all, Dion Houghton, one time Sales Director, are to be congratulated on the work.

One can only have the greatest admiration for the vision, knowledge, energy and enthusiasm of my forbears. At the same time ones own feelings are tinged with more than a hint of sadness to think that such a successful and proud company is effectively no longer in business as a manufacturer of engines, but today is simply reduced to a Parts Supply Company. How it has come about is covered in the book and whilst mistakes have been made along the way, – and what Company and employees haven't made mistakes, – would the result have been any different? With continued willing and enthusiastic owners there is no doubt that the life of the Company could have been extended, but the end result would probably have been the same. With the demise of the independent UK bus and truck manufacturers, basically by absorption by European engine and truck/bus manufacturers, and American manufacturers using American engines, there was nowhere else to go. Certainly the non-automotive side could not have kept the organisation running. To this situation should be added the cost of making engines comply with ever more stringent regulations, particularly with regard to gaseous emissions, these costs to be borne over a relatively small number of engines meaning that the final cost of the finished product was no longer acceptable.

Perhaps the biggest compliment that can be paid to my forbears and their designs is that LXB engines are still being remanufactured for hard, commercial applications. LW engines are a fairly frequent sight in our own workshops and even L3 engines, the oldest of which we have fully remanufactured here having been built in 1934. What better visible compliment could any Company have?

Paul Gardner, Patricroft, April 2002.

C A M D E N   M I N I A T U R E   S T E A M   S E R V I C E S

INVOICE

BARROW FARM,
RODE,
SOMERSET
BA11 6PS

Tel: 01373 830151   Fax: 01373 830516
VAT Reg. GB 349 4523 36

INVOICE TO:

Mr A B Bradshaw
Sweetbriar Cottage
Eyeworth Road
Wrestlingworth Sandy
Beds
SG19 2HG

Invoice No: 97784

Invoice Date: 17.05.2004

Your Customer No: 3359

Your Reference:

DELIVER TO:

Mr A B Bradshaw
Sweetbriar Cottage
Eyeworth Road
Wrestlingworth Sandy
Beds
SG19 2HG

ORD. QTY.	DESCRIPTION	TO FOLLOW	QTY. DEL.	UNIT PRICE	TOTAL PRICE
1	Gardner - Legendary Engineering Excell		1	24.50	24.50
1	Post & Packing		1	4.65	4.65

FAO: MR A B BRADSHAW

SWEETBRIAR COTTAGE
EYEWORTH ROAD

WRESTLINGWORTH
SANDY
Bedfordshire

SG19 2HG

Con.No:3001321000343l

Weight   1
Parcel   1
Tel.
Ref.   97784
AltRef

18/05/2004

NEXT DAY

HP

STEVENAGE

SENDER: CAMDEN MINIATURE STEAM SERVICES
(E69564/BA11 6PS)

INTRODUCTION

If a list of outstanding British engineering companies of the twentieth century were compiled then the name of L.Gardner & Sons Limited would rightly feature in the top few. Gardner's was by no means the biggest, nor was its name as prominent and widely known to the public as some of its contemporaries, but the achievements in diesel engine design and manufacturing of this Patricroft family firm were truly pioneering.

In the year 1929 Gardner's perfected a relatively small internal combustion engine that ran on diesel fuel which was directly injected into its cylinders. It was a worldwide first for an engine of its size and within a couple of years the concept had been extended to the first purpose built automotive power unit of this type. This was the renowned Gardner LW engine series, which was also revolutionary in its use of lightweight aluminium alloys. Moreover, the basic design was so good from inception that LW engines remained in production for forty-two years with only minor improvements.

Because diesel fuel was more economical than petroleum spirit for most of last century, and especially in the early thirties, there was a huge market for reliable and efficient diesel engines. At first they were bought to replace petrol units in buses, coaches, and lorries. Soon, diesel engines became the only choice for cost conscious transport companies. Gardner's also had an unrivalled reputation for quality engineering, so their engines were the preferred option of operators purchasing heavy commercial vehicles from chassis builders that did not manufacture their own engines. Such was the demand for Gardner engines that order books were continually full and waiting lists long.

If the Gardner reputation became established through its diesel engines it was only because there was sixty years of engineering evolution, expertise, and experience preceding its monumental achievements of the thirties. This was already an established company and had been making many kinds of engines since 1894. These were used for all manner of tasks including marine auxiliary, and marine main propulsion. Much later, rail traction also became an important market for Gardner's. Neither was this a purely 'home-market' concern, it exported to over forty countries.

For much of its existence members of the Gardner family, many of who were engineers par excellence, ran the company. Some of them could also be quite irascible! Eventually, after over a century of independence, L. Gardner & Sons Limited became part of a much larger company on the last day of 1977.

Whenever road transport of the twentieth century is analysed and discussed the contributions made by Gardner's remains paramount. Reliability, longevity, economy. These traits will forever be associated with a name revered by many. Sadly, Gardner engines are no longer made, but remnants of the company still exist.

This book covers the history of L. Gardner & Sons Limited from its beginning to the period when diesel engine manufacturing was phased out, and contains much information never previously published.

FOUNDING A FAMILY DYNASTY

In the year 1840 a baby boy was born in Manchester whose family name would one day epitomise engineering of the highest quality. That middle period of the 19th century was the time of the second great phase of the Industrial Revolution. This baby, named Lawrence, was the second son of Thomas Gardner, a miller, and his wife Jane. Lawrence grew-up in a wonderfully vibrant period of industrial innovation and expansion. For those were the years of the first railways pioneered by George and Robert Stephenson, and Isambard Kingdom Brunel, household names even then and still exalted over 150 years later. From tentative beginnings the railway system grew rapidly and within a generation most of Britain's major cities and towns had rail links.

With railways came prosperity to ambitious individuals and especially those possessing manufacturing and engineering skills. Manchester became not only the centre of the cotton industry, but also one of the engineering workshops for the world. At first this expertise grew out of mechanisation of the hundreds of cotton mills located within 10 miles of the city centre in

the mid to late 1800s. As and when other industries were established and modernised Manchester's engineering firms were able to supply machinery, not just locally, but throughout the country via the railways. When the Manchester Ship Canal was completed in 1894, Manchester and surrounding towns had a gateway to the world for their wares.

It can only be imagined how all this activity affected the adolescent Lawrence Gardner. As he was obviously attracted to engineering those must have been exciting times for him. Unfortunately little about his early life has been recorded, so it is not known where he served his apprenticeship and learned his trade. Wherever it was and whoever took young Lawrence under his wing did it well, because he became an exceptionally capable engineer. In due course his sons and grandsons would inherit his brilliant talent.

By the age of 21 Lawrence Gardner had married Anne Kynaston whose family were also millers. Even with his wife and growing family to support, Lawrence was confident enough, and had saved sufficient capital, to start his own business. This was when he was 28 years old

in 1868. His first premises were rather basic and cramped, being located in adjoining cellars under four houses in Duke Street, off Stretford Road Manchester. Machinery such as a boiler and lathe had to be lowered into the cellars through a trapdoor in the pavement. Their weight was supported by pulley blocks on wooden planks protruding from a bedroom window and it is recorded that some paving stones were damaged! Lawrence Gardner styled himself simply as a "machinist", with no particular speciality. But work was plentiful in this busy industrial city and in addition to being a manufacturer Lawrence acted as a consulting engineer to other companies. Even so, this was a difficult period and the fledgling concern nearly floundered. Lawrence, Anne, and their children lived in one of the houses above the workshops and the others were sub-let. This income was vital for keeping the tiny business solvent and when two of the tenants withheld their rent Gardner's enterprise was seriously threatened. The property's landlord was about to foreclose and auction the machinery, the only assets Lawrence had. Fortunately the business must have had potential because Lawrence obtained a building society loan, allowing him to buy the property. Nevertheless, for some time to come the rental income of tenants was vital in meeting mortgage repayments.

In due course Gardner's started to gain a reputation for the quality of work and meticulous attention to detail. Within a few more years Lawrence had outgrown his underground workshops and a new factory was constructed in 1884, nearby in Cornbrook Park Road. This was a two-storey building totalling 2,600 square feet. Soon he was employing twelve men there and this number gradually increased. When Lawrence's eldest sons reached their teens they began to learn the trade under their father's tutelage.

Gardner as a firm was prospering and from being solely jobbing, general engineers willing and able to tackle any small to medium sized task, Lawrence started designing his own machines. The diversity of production was fascinating. Along with sewing machines, moulds and vulcanizers for rubber tyres, it also included bread dough mixers, cardboard box folders, dovetailing machines, coffee roasters (two sizes), and dentist chairs made for The Dental Manufacturing Company. Coffee roasters consisted of four horizontal drums rotating above gas flames. The drums were belt-driven from a hot air engine. Components for these and other machines were made in-house if possible. Castings were bought from a Sheffield foundry with the patterns being made and supplied by Gardner's. The rough castings were machined

and finished when they arrived at the works. Gears were cut and filed and everything was made to the highest of standards. This policy was maintained as the firm prospered to great heights in subsequent years; especially after Gardner's built their own foundry.

With the Gardner engineering business on a sound footing Lawrence, Anne, and their eight children moved to house named "Newlands" on the Manchester to Irlam road. There were six boys and

Lawrence Gardner, founder of a firm in 1868 that went on to become the embodiment of the finest of British engineering practices. From modest beginnings, with just a few workers, L. Gardner & Sons Limited expanded to become one of Manchester's biggest employers with some 3,000 employees by the time of its centenary.

two girls and the boys all worked for the company founded by their father. It was truly a family firm, and this dynasty was guaranteed by the next generation. The children of Lawrence and Anne were:

JANE: She never married, remaining at home to help her mother look after the boys.

ELIZABETH: She married one T. Wilkinson and their son Frank Gardner Wilkinson worked for L. Gardner & Sons Limited, becoming Company Secretary and Director.

THOMAS H: The eldest son who had worked on railways before running the company after his father's death. He was a good engineer. His children were Eric, who became Managing Director of L. Gardner & Sons Ltd., and Dorothy who married a Dr. Staley. Mr Tom, as he was known was the real brains behind engine design and development.

EDWARD: Along with Tom, he was also a Whitworth Scholar. He married Connie Stott and was known as "Uncle Ned". He helped Tom and assisted with experimental engine testing.

JOSEPH: He developed the machine tools side of the business. He married Maude Stott, (Connie's sister), and they had two sons J. Hugh S, and John K. Both sons later became Joint Chief Designers and Managing Directors. Joseph was also involved with both T and J Type engines design, and later the L2 engine.

ERNEST: He fulfilled what today would perhaps be described as a public relations role, in that he looked after visitors and he was a fluent French speaker. He had two sons Tommy and Teddy who both became engineers with the family firm. They designed and produced a prototype small diesel engine, but it was never put into production. In later years Ernest unfortunately took to drink.

WILLIAM: Concentrated on the electrical side of production such as dynamos, then oil burners for the semi-diesel engines, and finally fuel "sprayers" (injectors). He had one son, Robert, who became an accountant.

LAWRENCE: Sadly he fell from a window when young and was permanently crippled. He worked alongside William on his projects. Lawrence was very interested in astrology.

Lawrence Gardner died aged only 50 in 1890, and twenty-two years after founding his company. He left the business to his wife Anne, and their eldest son Thomas Harry returned to supervise the factory. Thomas and his brother Edward were Whitworth Scholars at Manchester Victoria University. There had been a total of thirty engineering scholarships estab-

lished there by Sir Joseph Whitworth, himself a renowned engineer who had invented the screw thread that was named after him. Despite having worked with Lawrence, Thomas had not always been in agreement with his father, so he had worked on the railways to broaden his experience. He was regarded as a fine engineer, and it is often a good idea to learn how things are done elsewhere. This experience was to stand him in good stead as he prepared to propel his family's firm towards the twentieth century and embark on a completely new range of products.

SITES OF GARDNER'S WORKS IN THE OLD TRAFFORD AND CORNBROOK DISTRICTS OF MANCHESTER

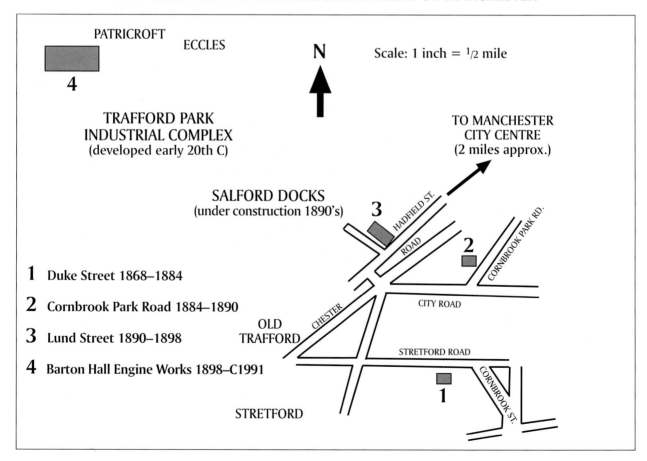

1 Duke Street 1868–1884

2 Cornbrook Park Road 1884–1890

3 Lund Street 1890–1898

4 Barton Hall Engine Works 1898–C1991

SHAPING THE FIRM'S FUTURE

Thomas Gardner was in his thirtieth year when he took responsibility for his family's firm. This was a similar age to Lawrence, his father, when he took the risk of founding the business. But not only was Thomas a gifted engineer in his own right, he had also received a fine education. Described as a man of drive, Thomas had found it difficult to work with his father, as sons and fathers often discover, so he decided to work elsewhere to broaden his experience. The knowledge he gained on the railways honed his engineering and management skills, leaving him well prepared for the burden of responsibility when the call came, albeit in the saddest of circumstances.

With his brother Edward, Thomas entered into a partnership with their mother. Cash books have survived showing that Anne Gardner was paid just over £2 per week for the next ten years, with Tom receiving slightly over £3 weekly, and Edward almost £3. But Stella Machine Works, as their Cornbrook Park Road factory was called, was now too small and another move became necessary. In November 1890 Gardner's re-located to a larger building nearby in Lund Street. Simply named "Gardner's Engineering Works" the office address was actually given as Hadfield Street. This is the main road off which Lund Street is located. The new factory kept eighty men fully employed but Thomas and Edward spotted an opportunity for their activities to

An interesting costing dating from April 1891 for a Robinson's 6 inches cylinder Patent Gas Engine. Note the letter heading with particular reference to the electrical equipment that was an important part of Gardner's business then.

become more specialised. General engineering was still important and dentists' chairs continued to provide steady work for some time. In fact 106 were made at Lund Street between 1891 and 1894 and Gardner's incorporated their own ideas into improving the design. Patents were granted in 1891 (number 7044), and another one, (number 14508) in 1892 was for hydraulically raising and lowering the chair. As a spin-off from this equipment for the Dental Manufacturing Company Gardner's also produced tools for making dentures.

The final decade of the nineteenth century continued to be an exciting time for mechanical progress. Being young men, the Gardner brothers would have been keenly aware of two highly significant engineering achievements of their era. In the year 1885 Karl Benz succeeded in propelling his motor tricycle with a 1 litre, single cylinder, horizontal internal combustion engine. It had taken 25 years, since Levoir in 1860 had produced the first practical internal combustion engine. Thereafter, by comparison, progress was rapid. Another momentous occasion was the switching-on of the

world's first electricity generating station at Godalming in September 1881. This was followed a few months later in 1882 with the first such facility for supplying electric power to those members of the public who could afford it. Michael Faraday had first demonstrated the principles of electricity generation way back in 1831. Once reliable electricity supplies became available, and coupled with the invention of the electric motor, industrial production was revolutionised to an even greater extent than it had been by harnessing steam power and building railways. Gardner's explored both these areas in the early 1890s.

All early electricity generating stations were usually small municipal affairs built for street lighting and tramways propulsion. Until electricity became more readily available to industry and the public by distribution through cable networks, many industrial premises had dynamos installed. These could be either driven from existing line shafting within a cotton mill, for example, or they could have their own prime mover such as a small steam, or gas engine. Consequently, as the merits of electricity became recognised there was a healthy demand for dynamos.

A hand written record book exists showing that Gardner's started making dynamos in 1892. The first was completed on 31st October, designated a 'No.1' machine. It generated single-phase current of 110 volts and was rated for 1.54 Kilowatts. (1,540 Watts). A couple of months later a second dynamo was finished and this was a '0' machine of 100 volts and 800 Watts. The following year, 1893, saw another seventeen dynamos produced although one was fitted as an electric motor and exported to Paris for

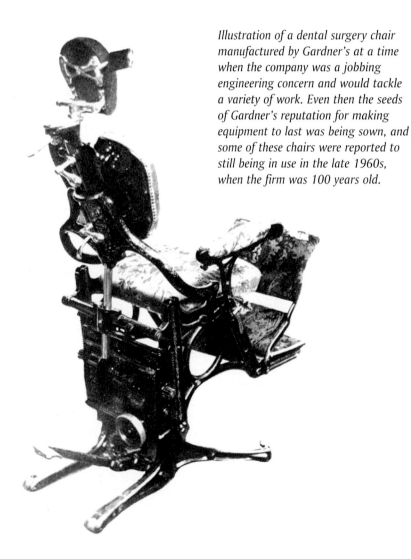

Illustration of a dental surgery chair manufactured by Gardner's at a time when the company was a jobbing engineering concern and would tackle a variety of work. Even then the seeds of Gardner's reputation for making equipment to last was being sown, and some of these chairs were reported to still being in use in the late 1960s, when the firm was 100 years old.

driving a pump. The other sixteen machines ranged in size from a '000' unit of 210 Watts to a 'No.8' of 24 Kilowatts. The following table records the quantity of Gardner dynamos made until production ceased in 1901. Some of these were quite large, weighing as much as three tons.

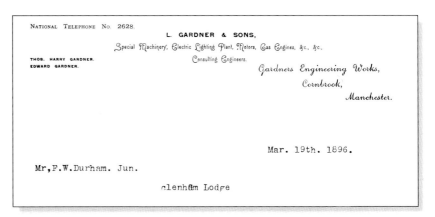

1892	2
1893	17
1894	25
1895	22
1896	21
1897	20
1898	23
1899	20
1900	3
1901	6
Total	159

A simple letterhead from 1896 listing only Thomas and Edward Gardner as partners, although their mother Anne was also co-owner of the firm. Gas engines now had been included in the listing of equipment made.

The earliest record of a serial number being applied to a dynamo was 75, allocated to a size '00' machine of 520 Watts completed on 16th June 1893. Thereafter numbering appeared to be haphazard until 21st March 1894 when another Gardner dynamo was given a serial number. This was 84, although the record book shows that a further twelve electrical machines had been produced since number 75, and by the time number 84 appeared twenty-one dynamos had been made in total. By May 1894 the early Gardner internal combustion engines were in production and they will be discussed later. The first was given serial number 81 and the significance, or otherwise, of commencing numbering of both dynamos and engines in the 80s is not revealed.

In August 1895 the archives intriguingly show that a "special steam dynamo" was made and it was coupled to a "Gardner steam engine". It was only a small machine of 200 Watts and it is believed to have been used internally at Lund Street for lighting part of the factory. Could it have also been possible that Gardner's were 'hedging their bets' and were experimenting with steam engines as well as internal combustion engines? The steam engine in question had been made by the brothers for driving the works, but they perhaps decided the future lay with internal combustion engines.

Gardner's last dynamo was serial number 264 made in 1901. By then demand for Gardner internal combustion engines was growing and there were other specialist, larger electrical machinery manufacturers emerging. Gardner dynamos were made in quite small quantities in various sizes, so standardisation of components was difficult and no doubt these were expensive machines to produce compared with those from emerging specialised electrical engineering concerns. Incidentally, the ledger does not show any machines against serial numbers 131 to 149 inclusive, so it is feasible that a few numbers were never allocated.

As has been mentioned Gardner's were exporting as early as 1893 and several dynamos were despatched to distant parts of the globe, including Nova Scotia and Shanghai, as well as neighbouring France.

It will be realised from the foregoing that Gardner's were first class jobbing engineers by the early 1890s. What really set the firm on its way to fame, success, and prosperity was becoming involved with internal combustion engines. Probably five years or so before the first dynamo appeared, Gardner's began manufacturing a patented design of hot air engine, known as a Robinson Hot Air Engine. Messrs. A.E. & H. Robinson, located in the Beswick district of Manchester, designed and sold industrial catering equipment such as frying ranges, potato peelers and chippers. Some of these needed a simple, cheap rotary motion so Horace Robinson designed and patented three sizes of hot air engines. Their power outputs ranged from one-fortieth to five eighths of one horsepower. Hot air engines could be used to drive small dynamos. The three sizes were known as '4', '5', or '6' engines for dynamos of 30 or 60 "lamps" and so on. The biggest weighed as much as 12 hundredweights. It is quite

A Robinson's Patent Hot Air Engine made by Gardner's. Whilst this design was not very efficient it was simple and reliable. Power output of this No.4 type was a tiny one eleventh of one horsepower at 150–210 rpm. It was however, a substantial machine, weighing almost 5 hundredweights. The firebox could burn either coal or coke, and a gas-fired version was also available at an extra cost of £1!

A No.5 Hot Air Engine producing one quarter of one horsepower at 150–190 rpm, and with a chain driven pump. Total weight was almost 10 hundredweights. It could raise 500 gallons of water per hour from a depth of 30 feet, or 150 gallons an hour from 100 feet.

possible that some of Gardner's smallest dynamos were driven by Robinson Hot Air Engines, also made by Gardner's. Robinson's had no machining facilities of their own so they sought suitable engineering companies locally. Gardner's, as jobbing engineers, were one of those successful in tendering for this work. These hot air engines were very simple machines, with heat being obtained by burning coke or 'Town Gas' in a firebox. There was a large piston of 10 inches bore and stroke, and a typical machine ran at 170 rpm. Power outputs were low, and thermal efficiencies were poor, but they were reliable and needed little maintenance. In addition to driving small dynamos they were installed in some large, remote establishments such as country houses, for pumping water.

Test reports prove that Mr Tom devoted some time to increasing the efficiency of these devices, mainly by improving the "regenerator", which was really the heart of the engine. Gardner's obviously made a good job of Robinson's engines and as early as 1888 they were awarded a gold medal at a trade fair. The citation complemented the firm on its "OUTSTANDING HOT AIR ENGINES". They sold well for several years and actually remained in production until the mid-1920s, but no doubt Gardner's realised that their own future would not be determined by producing such basic engines to a patented design for another company.

Concurrent with production of complete Robinson Hot Air Engines, Gardner's were also manufacturing components for a Robinson Patent Gas Engine. By the year 1890 all cities and larger towns had 'Town Gas' supplies. 'Town Gas' was obtained by heating coal in retorts with the ensuing combustible gas being stored and piped to consumers. Other useful by-products of this process included ammonia, coal tar, and coke. Gas engines were simple internal combustion engines using 'Town Gas' as fuel. In rural districts where 'Town Gas' was not available the hot air engine was a viable option until machines capable of running reliably on liquid fuels were developed.

Robinson's required more power for some of their equipment so they designed a series of gas engines. The components for these were again subcontracted to local machine shops, including Gardner's. Their first order was for three 0.5 bhp gas engines costing £10.10 shillings each, as opposed to £6 each for hot air engines. It would appear that Robinson's assembled their own gas engines from pre-machined and finished components supplied by Gardner's. A costing dated April 1891 shows that Gardner's charge for making items for a 6 inches cylinder Robinson Gas Engine was £24–13 shillings. Parts were to be supplied at the cost price of raw materials, which was 20.5% of the total. Labour amounted to 44.8%, and factory overheads 9.2%, plus a mark-up of 25.5%, calculated only on labour and overheads. There was no crankshaft included in the calculations, so Robinson's must have had another supplier for this particular component. Gardner's submitted different quotations to Robinson's for this work and this resulted in some discussions between would be supplier and purchaser. Two letters about this from Gardner's to Robinson's in January 1892 are reproduced verbatim.

Jan. 6 1892

Messrs. A.E. & H. Robinson,

Gentlemen,

We have pleasure in quoting you for 6" cyl. patent gas engine – valve box made up as in the 4½"cyl. engine just delivered, to include two turned flywheels but not including the standards, you supplying the crankshaft, we to find all other material except ignition apparatus, eccentric rod, and ratchet wheel for Twentysix pounds per engine for an order of two -£26.0.0.

In considering this quotation will you let us remind you that of the above £8.0.0. is absorbed by the two flywheels.

This £26.0.0 corresponds to the £32.5.0. handed to you this afternoon showing a reduction of £6.5.0.

We submit this low quotation in the hope that it will facilitate the "bringing out" of these engines and in the hope that we shall in time be able to make these at this price with a profit ourselves wh. we do not anticipate on the first order and with a further hope that we shall be able to reduce the price.

You may rest assured that if we should find things turn out better than we expect at present we shall let you have the benefit of it.

Yours faithfully,

L. GARDNER & SONS.

Robinson's must have queried this quotation and quibbled about the price – (some things have always been the same in business!) Less than one week later Gardner's replied, pleading their case.

Contained in these letters are several important clues as to Gardner's policy in those days, and this strategy was maintained by subsequent generations of the Gardner family involved in the

Jan. 11 1892

Messrs. A.E. & H. Robinson.

Gentlemen,

We are sorry that our quotation is so much above what you consider a fair price for these 6" engines – We need scarcely trouble you further with explanation as to how we arrived at this quotation as they have been traversed to recently. We fear however that you are unfairly comparing our quoted price with what you deem to be a fair price based on the manufacturing prices of engines made by these large firms where they, in a manner "weave the engines". You want us to make two engines and our price is to compare favourably with say Crossleys who 6 or 8 years ago never had less than 30 engines being fitted up at once – one department one size, one sub-department one job and so on! What this 30 is become at present we are not informed.

We shall be pleased to do the principal machining at low rate but we certainly think it would be most unsatisfactory to both parties to work to quoted prices.

The flywheel pattern is ready to go in to the foundry will please write per bearer if we are to send it in at once.

Yours faithfully,
L. GARDNER & SONS

running of the company. They were reluctant to compromise on price, and the reference to "weave the engines" is surely a term for mass production, again something Gardner's never practised. The mention of Crossleys is interesting, they were near neighbours of Gardner's on the opposite side of Manchester city centre to Cornbrook, and they were early manufacturers of stationery gas engines. At this date they were obviously a much larger company than Gardner's.

Despite haggling over prices agreement was reached between the two companies. Robinson's Patent Gas Engines were assembled principally from Gardner made components until 1894. This involvement was opportune for Thomas and Edward Gardner. It provided an insight into the potential market for industrial internal combustion engines, and gave practical experience of making them. Mr Tom could not resist tinkering with these Robinson gas engines, improving their performance and efficiency. Arguably, but for the involvement with Robinson's, Gardner's might never have entered the internal combustion engine business. As his younger brothers came into the firm Mr Tom started to investigate his own engine designs.

The 5th May 1894 must have been a memorable and auspicious day for the Gardner family. Their very own, and first, internal combustion engine was completed and tested. Totally designed and built by Thomas and Edward to the Otto four-stroke cycle it was fuelled by 'Town Gas'. It was a horizontal layout, designated 'No.1' gas engine, developing 1 bhp at 350 rpm. This first genuine Gardner engine was

This is a No.6 Hot Air Engine of five-eighths horsepower at 140–170 rpm, again with a simple pump. Total weight was 18 hundredweights. These Hot Air Engines were still being made, and sold in Ireland in the early 1920s, and this size then cost £65 complete with its pump. It could raise 760 gallons per hour from 50 feet, or 380 gallons an hour from 100 feet.

used to drive a dynamo for providing lighting in the "small room" at Gardner's Engineering Works. A serial number, 81, was allocated to this engine and it is possible that many of the preceding eighty machines were hot air engines.

A second similar engine, number 82, was made and this had a larger cylinder bore of 3⅜ inches, an increase of ⅛ inch over the original. This was also used internally at the works. Six more similar engines with bores of 3½ inches were laid down in July 1894 for general sale. These were engines numbered 83 to 88 inclusive.

The notebooks of Thomas and Edward still exist and provide rather sparse details of the earliest engines made. After the first batch of engines was built the records do improve. The entry against engine number 88 reads: –

"was troublesome – had compression reduced by turning off piston – will only do 10 lights at 48 volts. To Bradford 22nd Sept."

A further lot of six engines were laid down in October 1894, followed by another six in December. In the same month the first 'No.3' engine, serial number 101, was produced. This had a bore of 5½ inches and it developed 3½ bhp at 250 rpm. In January 1895 the first Gardner 'No.2'

engine, with a 4½ inches bore was introduced. Theoretically it should have produced 2 bhp at 300 rpm, but it was obviously a good one because this prototype managed an output of 2.7 bhp. It was retained at the works and was used to assist the powerhouse steam engine.

All these gas engines had hot tube ignition. The tube was connected to the combustion chamber and a gas flame in a chimney around the tube heated it. Tubes appear to have been temperamental and the performance of a reluctant engine could be improved simply by changing the tube.

Each gas engine had its own idiosyncrasies. For example recorded against 'No.1' engine, serial number 105: –

"This engine was remarkably free from all defects. Started very well, chimney at

top of post, although compression was the same as the others, viz 60 lbs. Piston was very clean".

Other entries in the book show that piston rusting was causing problems and that pistons would not run clean until the rings were bedded in. One problem with 'Town Gas' as fuel is that water vapour is a by-product of combustion, hence rusting on cast iron pistons.

Typical gas consumption figures including the gas flame for the ignition tube worked out at approximately 30 cubic feet per hour per bhp for smaller engines and 27.5 cubic feet per hour per bhp for larger units.

Other sizes of engines were gradually introduced into the range available. On 25th May 1895 the first 'No.0' engine, serial number 132 was manufactured with a bore of 2½ inches and developing 0.55

bhp at 450 rpm. Later the bore for this type was standardised at 2¾ inches to provide 0.75 bhp. Later in 1895, on 4th October the original 'No.4' type. Serial number 148 was started at teatime and left to run all night. This was bigger than anything previously made, having a 6 inches bore and producing 5.08 bhp at 250 rpm. Gardner's were none too pleased with it because a note reads: –

"This engine is not running as nicely as the other sizes – it bucks and thumps".

To improve its running the brothers reduced the compression pressure to 45 lbs by cutting "the dead head completely off the piston" (by pulling round a lathe by hand). This cured the problem and number 148 was tested by driving the factory for one month. Afterwards it was painted blue and sold to a customer in London!

To round off the development activities for 1895 a 'No.1A' engine, serial number 164, was tested on 27th November. This had a bore of 4 inches and produced 1.5 bhp at 330 rpm. So, in the eighteen months between May 1894 and November 1895 Gardner's had introduced six basic engine types. An even bigger design came along in 1896 when a 'No.6' was built with an 8 inches bore. This was rated at 9.5 bhp at 200 rpm.

Within the first two years of internal combustion engine production Gardner's had made almost one hundred machines. Some were retained for internal use at the factory, but the vast majority were sold to clients mainly in the Lancashire and London areas. The first known engine to be directly exported was a 'No.2' that went to Barcelona in 1896. This was the precursor of further exports to

Spain, and France also became a good export market.

There can be no doubts that by 1896 Gardner's were becoming well known for their gas engines. While they were still a relatively small manufacturer in a rapidly growing market their reputation for quality was already becoming established. Gardner's realised that they needed to expand their range of engines by introducing a successful liquid fuel design. Such engines were much cheaper to run than gas engines. Their first experiments with paraffin oil (kerosene) had begun in September and October 1896 with a converted 'No.1' gas engine (serial number 229) but these tests were soon "dropped for want of time". They resumed again in April 1897 and by the end of the year four 'oil' engines of various sizes were sold. The ignition system for these engines was based on that of the gas types and a hot tube was retained. A measured amount of paraffin oil was fed into a vaporising chamber heated by a pressure lamp. The vaporised oil, mixed with air, was drawn into the cylinder by the descending piston and the mixture of air and oil vapour was compressed by the piston on its next stroke. Ignition was completed by the hot tube. In principle this was similar to the Priestman oil engine, the first successful engine of this type introduced in 1885.

These early Gardner oil engines had an in-house designed fuel pump which accurately delivered the quantity of fuel needed for each compression stroke. The amount of fuel decided the power output of the engine, and also influenced the smooth running of the engine. Too much fuel was wasteful and also caused a rapid build-up of carbon deposits on the piston and in the

cylinder. At this date paraffin oil was mainly used for burning in oil lamps and for other domestic uses such as cooking stoves. Viscosity and quality was variable so petroleum spirit, being a more volatile and lighter distillate of crude oil offered greater potential for consistency as a fuel. In 1897 another 'No.1' engine, serial number 338 was tested fuelled by petroleum spirit. The notes record the following: –

"was fitted up as a spirit engine on Wednesday 14th April, and started at 8.30 pm. Started without difficulty and ran very well at full load till 10.45 pm. Engine appeared perfect. Next morning, in starting, the engine fired backwards right out of my hands and of course exhausted through the inlet valves."

As a result of this incident Gardner's fitted a non-return valve in the air inlet manifold so that any future backfires would not blow petrol out of the vaporiser. Hot tube ignition was still used and a 'fuel feeder' was the means of mixing petrol vapour and air. Experiments with magneto and spark plug ignition were in progress and the first in a series of carburettors was under development

Petroleum spirit consumption was calculated at 0.944 pints per bhp per hour, excluding the lamp for heating the tube, or 1.075 pints per bhp per hour with the tube lamp.

On the 19th December 1896 Gardner's made their first multi-cylinder engine, a two-cylinder version of a 'No.6'. The cylinders lay side by side and it was designated 'No.6/6', serial number 279. After a satisfactory test lasting six hours (were Gardner's superstitious by any chance?) it was delivered to a customer at Colne, Lancashire, on 23rd December. Recorded against it is the comment "singularly free from all faults".

This engine was significant for another reason because consecutive serial numbering stopped at 279 and resumed again at 300. Thereafter engines were given only even numbers until 998, when consecutive numbering was re-introduced. This was possibly a sales gimmick to make customers believe more engines had been sold.

From the outset of internal combustion engine production it seems as if Gardner's had a range of various sizes planned. Whether every engine was built against a specific order has not been recorded, but it would appear to have been the case. This view is supported by the late appearance of their first 'No.5' type on 7th August 1897. This had a bore of 7 inches and it was rated for 8.6 bhp at 220 rpm. It was serial number 476 and "it ran very well", being exported to France. One year later and a 'No.7' gas engine was tested. With a bore of 9 inches and stroke of 15 inches it was comparatively speaking, something of a monster, producing 15.74 bhp at 200 rpm.

By the year 1898 the Gardner family could have been in no doubts that their future lay with the production of internal combustion engines. Plans had already been made for the construction of a purpose built factory that would allow them to fulfil their destiny. Within a couple of years a new century would dawn and Gardner's would be ready to meet the industrial challenges it promised.

ENGINE PRODUCTION 1894 to 1898

TYPE	1894	1895	1896	1897	1898
'No.0'		7	12	31	10
'No.1'	20	36	44	71	107
'No.1A'		7	24	36	61
'No.1AV'					1
'No.2'		12	12	27	54
'No.3'	1	4	9	12	16
'No.4'		2	2	13	18
'No.4A'				4	7
'No.5'				3	13
'No.6'			1		5
'No.6/6'			1		1
'No.7'					2
TOTAL	21	68	105	197	295

CHAPTER
3

A NEW FACTORY
FOR A NEW CENTURY

As the nineteenth century drew to a close it was becoming obvious that the internal combustion engine was going to assume immense importance in the none too distant future. Already at that time the demand for this source of power was becoming insatiable, not only for industrial purposes but also for diverse forms of transport. The Gardner brothers realised that their firm's destiny was in this market and they also knew that their Lund Street facilities were unsuitable and too small if they were to capitalise on this untapped potential. Within six years of their previous move they needed to relocate again. Consequently in 1896 Gardner's purchased three acres of land at the eastern edge of Chat

Moss near Eccles. At the time this was still quite a rural district known locally as Patricroft. Within thirty years this area would almost be part of the massive industrial complex called Trafford Park as it expanded westwards from Manchester.

The site chosen was once an estate called Barton Old Hall. By an historical quirk the family that had title to the property had died out over 600 years earlier, but their name survived. Two other families, firstly the Booths, and then the Leigh's had long associations with the domain. Gardner's bought the land from the Leigh's, although the last building of any note to occupy the site was demolished twenty years previously.

Two years passed from buying the

estate until the new factory, which would be known as Barton Hall Engine Works, was ready for occupancy. Already the decision to move was justified because in the period between 1896 and 1898 production of Gardner engines almost trebled. Although there was demand and a market for these engines, a sales organisation to exploit this potential was required. As none of the Gardner brothers were salesmen, – they were all engineers, – another early decision made by Thomas and Edward had been to appoint an agency to do their selling.

In the year 1891 Gardner's selected the London based Norris and Henty to promote their goods. Norris and Henty would best be

When Norris & Henty Limited became agents for Gardner's in 1891 they soon incorporated an illustration of a Robinson's Hot Air Engine onto company letterheads. This example is believed to be from that same year.

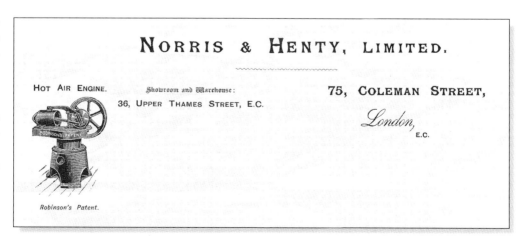

NORRIS & HENTY, LIMITED.

HOT AIR ENGINE.

Showroom and Warehouse:
36, UPPER THAMES STREET, E.C.

75, COLEMAN STREET,

London,
E.C.

Robinson's Patent.

described as "general factotums"; having contacts and the wherewithal to sell almost anything anywhere. The principals were Edward. H. Norris and Captain Charles G. Henty. The latter was the son of George Alfred Henty, well known then as an author of schoolboy Victorian adventure stories. Norris and Henty had offices at 75, Coleman Street, in the City of London, and a showroom and warehouse nearby at 36, Upper Thames Street. Within a few years the business generated by sales of Gardner engines would mean them dealing almost exclusively with Gardner products.

Initially Gardner's new facilities at Barton Hall were modest, occupying 2,046 square yards. The move, on 22nd April 1898, was partly financed by selling their patents and interests in dentist chairs when the Dental Manufacturing Company was itself bought by an American company. Further capital was raised in 1901 when the Gardner family partnership was dissolved and a limited liability company formed, into which their assets were conveyed. As a lasting tribute to their founding father, the family retained the name L. Gardner and Sons Limited, when they could just as easily have named the company "Gardner Brothers Limited". Authorised capital for the company was £50,000 (a large sum of money in 1901) in £1 shares. Half of these were 6% preference shares and half ordinary shares. Of the ordinary stock 12,000 were issued to members of the Gardner family and 12,000 preference shares were sold on the stock exchange. Control of the company remained very firmly in Gardner hands with all the brothers except William, who was still a minor, appointed to the Board of Directors.

The first years of last century saw an astonishing rate of expansion at Barton Hall. New buildings were constructed and additional tracts of land acquired. In 1908 a further 16,000 square yards were bought and in 1911 and 1912 an additional total of 57,000 square yards was leased. A foundry was built and equipped, enabling the company to be self-sufficient for its ferrous, bronze, and aluminium castings. This enabled their quality to be

✦ PRICE LIST. ✦

THE GARDNER OIL ENGINE
(HORIZONTAL TYPE.)

⤳ TERMS, &c. ⤶

The prices in the annexed list are for delivery at Patricroft.

Packing is charged extra, but two-thirds of the full amount will be allowed **solely on the condition** that the empties be returned to the works within **14 days**, carriage paid, undamaged, and with all holding down bolts.

Each Engine is sent out with water tank, exhaust box, lamp, oil tank, all necessary sundries for use in working, sundry spares, and set of spanners. All are included in list prices.

On receipt of an order for an engine, we send a blue print showing in full detail the foundation, connections, pipes, tanks, and the method of fixing generally. A book of instructions is afterwards sent out with the engine.

The makers do not bind themselves to details shown in the illustration.

⤳ TABLE OF PRICES, &c. ⤶

Code Word	No. of Engine	Effective working load B.H.P. (See Foot note.)	At Revs. per min.	Total Weight (nett) Cwts.	Kilos.	Total weight packed for Shipment (gross) Cwts.	Kilos.	Extreme dimensions of Engine with Fly-wheel. Length Ins.	Metr's	Width Ins.	Metr's	Fly-Wheel Diameter Ins.	Metr's	Width Ins.	M'm	Price
Hebe	0	½	450	2	102	2¾	139	32	0·81	16	0·40	18	0·45	3	76	£ 25
Hecla	1	1	350	3½	177	4¾	241	39	0·99	20	0·51	24	0·61	3	76	30
Hedron	1A	1½	320	6¼	318	8¼	419	46	1·17	31	0·79	30	0·76	4	101	40
Hegra	2	2	300	10¼	521	12	610	53	1·34	36	0·91	36	0·95	4	101	55
Hellas	3	3½	250	14½	737	17	864	64	1·62	39	0·99	39	0·99	5	127	75
Henan	4	4½	230	17	864	20½	1042	67	1·70	41	1·04	42	1·06	5	127	88
Hepris	4A	6	230	23	1168	28	1422	70	1·78	45	1·14	45	1·14	5	127	101
Heric	5	7½	220	29	1473	34½	1753	78	1·98	52	1·32	48	1·22	6	152	112
Hestro	6	9	200	39	1981	44½	2260	84	2·13	58	1·47	54	1·37	7	178	132
Hetro	7	12	190	54	2750	59	3004	94	2·39	61	1·55	57	1·45	7	178	150
Heva	8	15	190	57	2896	63	3302	100	2·54	63	1·60	60	1·52	7½ Two Fly-Wheels	190	168
Hexam	9	20	180	66	3353	76	3861	113	2·87	72	1·83	60	1·67	7½ Two Fly-Wheels	203	220
Heyter	6/6	18	200	63	3200	71	3607	114	2·89	58	1·47	54	1·37	7	178	240

NOTE.—No. 6/6 Engine is a double Engine—a cylinder at each end working on to one crank.

SUBJECT TO ALTERATION WITHOUT NOTICE. ALL PREVIOUS LISTS CANCELLED.

The above list of weights and dimensions has been carefully compiled, but the makers do not hold themselves responsible for any inaccuracy that there may be.

NOTE.—The powers of the engines as listed above are the powers that we consider advisable to quote. The actual maximum powers are considerably higher.

A Gardner's engine price list from April 1902 and all are horizontal types. The biggest, a Number 9 weighed over 3 tons. The code words were used at a time when sales orders would either be sent by telegram, or cablegram, and brevity was essential. For example if a sales representative ordered a "Henan", the factory would know exactly what was required.

RIGHT: *An example of early, small, Gardner horizontal engine that has survived to the present day. The high quality of the engineering employed in its manufacture is apparent.*

BELOW: *Early Gardner vertical engines were virtually up-ended horizontals with open crankshafts. These designs were only in production for 5 years, from 1898 until 1903, when new vertical types then had crankcases.*

strictly controlled. Gardner's were still looking to the future and yet more land, another 31,000 square yards, was secured for expansion in due course. By 1914 there was almost twenty-four acres comprising the site of Barton Hall Engine Works. By no means was it all covered with buildings at that date, about sixteen acres was still open space. But never again would another re-location be necessary for Gardner's.

The means of expansion was provided by the great success of Gardner engines. The brothers were very inventive and innovative and their machines were manufactured to the highest standards, creating the Gardner reputation for premium quality. They commenced with horizontal designs, but the future was with vertical types and the first Gardner vertical was a 'No.1AV', serial number 1084, made in 1898. It developed 1.8 bhp at 400 rpm. It was almost an up-ended horizontal with an open crankcase, and these early verticals became available in five sizes. They were superseded in 1903 when a fully enclosed crankcase design was introduced.

Incidentally, the new works had line shafting for driving its machinery and this was powered by a Gardner 'No.8' engine, which was

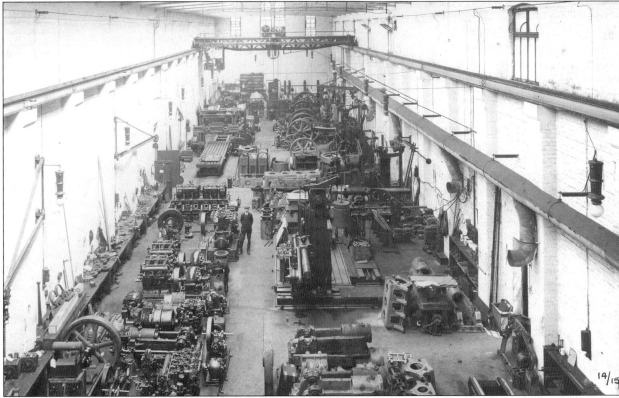

TOP: A view of the new Barton Hall Engine Works taken from Gorton Street, Patricroft, in 1906. Much of the scene is typical of industrial Manchester almost a century ago such as the cobbled roadway, and gas lamp.

ABOVE: An internal view of Barton Hall Engine Works showing the Testing and Shipping Bay, with horizontal and multi-cylinder vertical engines in view. The photograph was probably taken about 1914.

The Humber car owned by one of the Gardner brothers that was fitted with a Gardner '2BR' petroleum spirit engine. This twin-cylinder design produced 10 horsepower, but few were made and it was not a commercial proposition for motorcar manufacturers. The photograph dates from 1903.

converted from a 'No.7'. After six years driving the factory it was sold to a customer. Already the Gardner reputation for longevity was becoming established. It was also in 1898 that the earliest experiments were carried out with electrical ignition by coil and battery on a 'No.1' spirit engine, serial number 1038. This was only the tenth petrol engine made up to then, the preference being for gas and oil types. These fuels were more readily available because of their widespread usage for lighting and heating. Remember, motorcars were still quite rare and filling stations did not exist then. Petroleum spirit was sold from a variety of outlets as diverse as pharmacies and livery stables. The majority of car journeys undertaken were only local jaunts in vehicles owned by wealthier people. Often, suppliers delivered petrol to their homes in two gallons cans.

It can only be imagined what a hectic time it must have been at Gardner's at the turn of the century.

There was a huge market for engines and technological advances were rapid. The first decade of the twentieth century saw Gardner's introducing several new types. All the early engine ranges are listed in Appendix A, but the main developments were as described in the following paragraphs, with some of their distinguishing features.

Firstly, it is necessary to return briefly to 1898 when an interesting little engine was designed and produced. This was known as a '2BR' and it had two adjacent cylinders. Its intended application was as a motorcar power unit and one was certainly fitted into a Humber owned by one of the Gardner brothers. Sadly, this engine was one of the few commercial failures for Gardner's, probably because it was too expensive for fledgling motorcar builders.

Early Gardner vertical engines from 1899 were basically horizontals turned through 90 degrees to an upright format. They retained open crankshafts and designations ranged from 'No.0V' to 'No.5V', with some intermediate sizes, such as 'No.1AV'. These were replaced in 1903 by a series of verticals for smaller installations. Named simply as 'V' types they were relatively slow revving petrol or paraffin engines with power outputs varying from 1.75 bhp to 10 bhp. They had fully enclosed cranks and as well as being used in static applications they could also be mounted on trailers for providing a portable means of power. They were also used to drive air compressors or pumps. Later a marine version was introduced for small boats and barges.

One year before the revised single cylinder vertical engines came into production another series of verticals soon became recognised as one of the best of its era. This was the fabled Gardner 'M' Series and these engines were used for many applications. Almost as soon as they became available, they attracted the attention of marine engineers, and 'M' Series units became popular marine engines. This widespread acceptance by one of the most demanding engineering disciplines opened up another important market for Gardner's. 'M' Series engines also drove dynamos for lighting factories, theatres, and cinemas, as well as being connected

Price list for methylated spirits when Gardner's sought to buy directly from a distiller. Engine testing at Barton Hall had emptied all the local chemists of stocks of meths and a special licence had to be obtained to permit Gardner's to purchase in quantity.

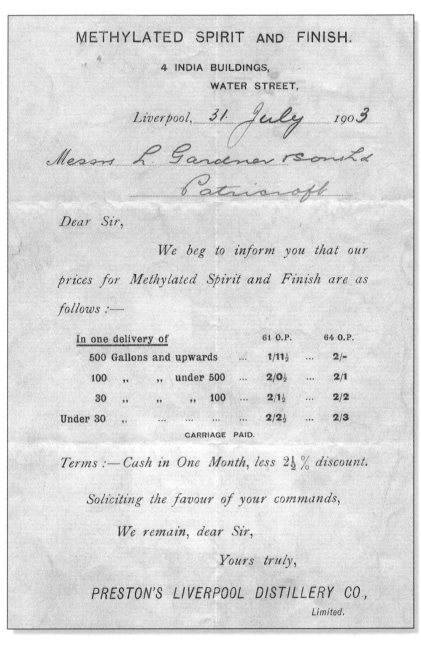

to air compressors, or pumps. They also provided the electricity for wireless stations. Gardner 'M' Series engines were one of the first universal power units. Another important feature of this design was that it set the precedent for an engine with an optional numbers of cylinders. In other words, a customer could specify how many cylinders he needed to best satisfy his power requirements. Gardner's maintained this policy of multi-cylinder engine ranges for the next half century at least. While they were not unique amongst major engine producers in doing this, Gardner's were undoubtedly the most successful and persevered with this strategy for longer than most.

Some Gardner records from this period are difficult to follow, and are somewhat confusing when trying to determine what engine series appeared exactly when. It could have been the case that so much development was taking place at the time there was an overlap of ideas. The 'M' Series could have originated as an engine range called 'HV', using either petrol or paraffin as fuel. Reference is made to these 'HV' types in the early 1900s and they were planned as single cylinder units in nine optional sizes, i.e. '1HV' to '7HV', with intermediates of '3AHV' and '4AHV'. Power outputs were from 5 bhp to 35 bhp, all at 800 rpm. It is recorded however, that these single cylinder engines were renamed 'BM' shortly after they were conceived. The first 'BM' engine, serial number 2954 was tested on 3rd October 1902.

Gardner 'M' Series units were faster revving engines than earlier horizontal and vertical types and they continued to utilise the four-stroke cycle. They had separately cast cylinders with water-cooling. They could use a variety of fuels including petrol or paraffin with magneto ignition; or oil, or Town Gas. The smallest of the family was the single cylinder 'BM' unit, producing 5 bhp, and a '2BM' was a two-cylinder engine and so on. 'DM' engines had larger bores and in 1906 the largest of the family was produced. This was an eight cylinder job designated '8SM'. It produced up to 300 bhp and it was the biggest

TOP: This picture shows the erecting bay for 'H' Type engines, which were larger designs of horizontals after 1910. The biggest of these were huge machines with massive flywheels.

ABOVE: Section of one of the machine shops at Barton Hall. The building and equipping of a brand new factory was a massive investment for the Gardner brothers and resulted in the family partnership being dissolved and a limited liability, public company, being formed. The Gardner family still retained control and after the initial move to Barton Hall Engine Works in 1898, further expansion on the site took place at regular intervals for the next 15 years.

RIGHT: The introduction of 'M' series engines in 1902 opened the door for Gardner's into the marine market. This is a 4KM of 8 inches bore by 9 inches stroke, and operating on the 4-stroke cycle it produced 75 bhp at 500 rpm. It ran on paraffin as fuel with lamp heated vaporizers.

BELOW: There were many applications other than marine installations where 'M' series engines were suitable. In the first quarter of the twentieth century many premises, including theatres, music halls, and early cinemas, as well as factories and mills, generated their own electricity. This was a 6KM producer gas engine used for driving a dynamo.

engine made by Gardner's at the time. It was 18 feet long and the crankshaft was made from two sections, bolted together in the centre. There were many 'M' Series variants such as 'FM', 'FHM', 'KM', 'KRM', and each of these could have different cylinder configurations.

All these 'M' Series engines were highly successful and were purchased by some government departments such as the Admiralty,

LEFT: A 2BM paraffin engine for driving a dynamo. Note the apparently massive flywheel relative to the size of the engine. BM, KM, and FHM engines were also popular coupled to dynamos as emergency lighting sets on board ships. Well-known ship builders fitting them included Swan Hunter, Vickers, B. Yarrow & Company, Cammell Laird & Company, and Armstrong Whitworth.

the War Office, and the India Office. Marine versions featured a Gardner designed speed governor which prevented a ship's propeller running wild when breaking the surface in rough seas. Gardner's were also quick to spot an opportunity for designing their own marine reversing gear to complement their engines. This they did in 1903 and it was available in sizes 1 to 6. Later a modified design known as 'GT'

BELOW: Gardner's soon started to produce marine reversing gear and their own unit was coupled to a 3KM paraffin engine in this picture. Gardner reversing gear was available in six sizes to be compatible with the power of the engine used.

RIGHT: A variety of fuels could be specified for Gardner 'M' series engines and this one was a 4FHM which principally ran on Town Gas, but was dual-fuelled and could run on petrol. One problem with Town Gas was that mains pressure was variable and if domestic demand was high, gas pressure dropped and engine performance was impaired.

BELOW: With the photographer of the time's penchant for removing all background details it is difficult to gauge the size of some of these Gardner 'M' series engines. This is a 4NM producer gas fuelled unit and its motion side is shown. Note the step to gain access to the walkway; indicating this was a big engine. This is confirmed by another view of the opposite side of this engine showing a three-rung ladder for climbing onto a plate level with the top of the crankcase.

reversing gear was introduced and it is believed three sizes were available. The Gardner reversing gear permitted full engine power to be applied when the vessel was running astern.

Many Gardner 'M' Series engines had prodigious working lives. The fishing smack *"Vineyard"* had a 55 bhp 'KM' fitted and spare parts were ordered for it 28 years after it was installed. A larger '6JM' unit in the Royal Mail vessel *"Lochinver"*, of 200 tons displacement, gave 20 years of reliable service.

One interesting little problem occurred during 1903 when Gardner's found it difficult to obtain methylated spirits for testing purposes. Some engines were designed to use alcohol, (methanol or demineralised methylated spirits), as fuel, particularly export orders destined for countries

LEFT: Here is a 4BCR engine that was paraffin fuelled, but was first started with petrol. Once it was warm it would run on paraffin with spark ignition. Gardner 4BCR engines were especially popular in lifeboats carried by ocean-going liners at the time of the "Titanic" disaster in 1912. Among many famous shipping lines of yesteryear using them, (or the 3DM option), were Barclay Curle, The Brocklebank Line, Bibby Brothers, Alfred Holt, and The White Star Line, owners of the "Titanic".

BELOW: A 2BCR petrol fuelled engine driving a dynamo as part of an electric arc-welding set. It has been mounted onto a skid and is complete with a large radiator and header tank.

Even though Gardner's had introduced a multi-cylinder 'M' series in 1902 there was still demand for single cylinder verticals for smaller installations, and a new 'V' range was introduced in 1903. Illustrated is a 5V paraffin engine, and these slow revving designs could also be specified to run on either petrol or Town Gas.

without gas supplies. Local chemists were running out of meths because of the demand from Barton Hall. Normal meths able to be bought over the counter was, and is, treated with an additive to discourage people from drinking it. Gardner's had to obtain a dispensation from Customs and Excise to enable them to purchase demineralised methylated spirits directly from a supplier, strictly for testing purposes.

Despite a great demand for 'M' Series, single cylinder 'V', and 'H' engines keeping the new factory and its growing workforce fully occupied, development was ongoing. Additional engine types were added to the Gardner catalogue later in the decade. The first full year with the 'M' series in production saw total output increase by almost 64%, from 480 units in 1902 to 785 engines in 1903. In the year 1908 Gardner's brought out their 'TP' series, which was available with four, six, or eight cylinders. One year later in 1909 they produced their only V configuration design. This was a two cylinder affair designated '2WT' (although one cylinder could be removed to make a '1WT' engine!). This was an air-cooled engine with a bore of 4½ inches, supplied to the GPO for drying out cable ducting.

By the year 1910 the original horizontal types were in need of updating. The smaller ones in the range were re-worked to become 'F' types. They were still available for different kinds of fuels. Petrol fuelled engines now had high-tension magneto ignition in place of hot tubes and 'F' types had power outputs of between 0.75 and 14 bhp. They were mainly installed for driving small dynamos, or compressors used by gas companies

for pumping Town Gas through their pipelines. A Gardner 'F' was sold to Buckingham Palace and several more were used in London for lighting bridges across the River Thames.

Larger horizontals became 'H' types and the biggest produced 70 bhp at 190 rpm. The 'H' range had detachable cylinder liners and white metal bearings. They were generally oil-fuelled and they were started by compressed air. After the fuel supply was turned off to stop the engine

the last few piston strokes charged a storage cylinder with air for the next time the engine was needed. 'F' types could also be modified to run on other fuels, including "poor gas", which was producer gas manufactured at the same site as the engine installation. "Poor gas" was a substitute for Town Gas where supplies of the latter were not available. It was also used by some larger factories whose owners decided it was a cheaper option than Town Gas.

With the trusty horizontals updated Gardner's then introduced a new petrol engine series in 1910, which was becoming a prolific year for them. This was their 'CR' series and it was intended for smaller marine applications such as in launches, pleasure craft, and cutters. 'CR' engines were faster revving than 'M' Series, but they too could be ordered with differing numbers of cylinders that were separately cast.

ABOVE: Shown here is a 3V Town Gas fuelled engine with a massive flywheel to smooth out its relatively slow revolutions and enable it to produce a steady output of electricity. It is coupled to a General Electric Co. dynamo.

LEFT: Gardner's first step along the road to compression ignition Diesel engines came with the introduction of two-stroke semi-diesels designed to incorporate the ideas of Ackroyd-Stuart. The first 'T' and 'VT' types appeared in 1913 and there were many versions produced in subsequent years. This is a 7VT heavy oil engine (diesel fuel) for driving a W.H. Allen & Sons Ltd. dynamo. The blowlamp for heating the antechamber when starting is visible, along with the fuel feed pipe to the injector, or sprayer.

RIGHT: One of the smaller Gardner marine petrol engines, a 2ACR that produced 8.5 bhp at 1000 rpm.

BELOW: Gardner's were exporting to most countries within the former British Empire from the late nineteenth century and this 4CR engine was in service in New Zealand.

TOP: One of the larger, relatively high-speed 'CR' marine petrol engines, and this 3DCR is coupled to a Gardner 2E reversing gear. The removable side plate on the crankcase to allow access to the crankshaft bearings for annual inspection is prominent. This was a Board of Trade regulation for marine installations.

ABOVE: This was the "Kwang Su" ferry, owned by APC Co. of Shanghai. Built in 1911 this craft was originally fitted with twin 4FHM engines which propelled the 66 ft long, 12 tons, boat at 10.5 knots. These engines were later replaced with twin 4T4 semi-diesel units, each of 48 bhp output.

Seawater was used for cooling purposes, courtesy of large water jackets, cast in one piece with, and around the cylinders. These cooling jackets were sufficiently capacious to prevent salty deposits accumulating. Many famous shipping lines of the time specified 4BCR engines for ships' lifeboats.

It became a speciality of Gardner's to produce engines in series. Having decided on a suitable cylinder bore of, for example, 4 inches, a range would be designated 'BCR' and be available with either two, three or four cylinders. All parts were completely interchangeable with a cylinder from a 4BCR fitting a 2BCR engine. If more power was required another line-up, i.e. 'CCR' with 4.5 inches cylinder bore with various cylinders, was made available. Type 'DCR' engines had 5.5 inches bores and so on. This policy was continued with subsequent designs and fleet operators only needed minimal stocks of spare parts to keep several engines with differing cylinder numbers in service.

It has been recorded that at least one Gardner 'CR' engine achieved an incredible 50 years of service. This four-cylinder version was retrofitted into a 32 feet private launch named "Mascot" that was built in 1908 by Borwick & Sons of Windermere. Her owner used "Mascot" on the lake until 1921 when she was sold and renamed "Duchess". She was then used for pleasure trips on Lake Windermere until 1961. A tremendous achievement from an engine built 50 years before.

By 1912 the range of Gardner engines was truly vast and a sales catalogue for that year lists fourteen sizes of horizontals and no fewer than forty-nine different verticals. In total therefore, sixty-three distinct

ABOVE: A good view of some of the intricate engineering used by Gardner's on its engines. This is a 5VT semi-diesel with its fuel pump and sprayer prominent. Air was drawn into the cylinder through the circular, perforated filters positioned on top of the crankcase.

TOP RIGHT: Gardner 'T' series semi-diesel engines were a multi-cylinder range of varying cylinder dimensions. Shown here is a 4T6 and it is interesting to observe that its crankshaft was routed along a raised tunnel into the centre of the flywheel. A pump was also driven from the opposite end of the crankshaft.

BOTTOM RIGHT: 'VT' and 'T' type engines were similar but with subtle differences. This is one of the larger 'VT' versions, a 4/4 VT. Compared with the 4T6 it has a different design of antechambers and a larger flywheel. Various pumps are also driven from the front of the crankshaft.

ABOVE: In addition to being used as main marine propulsion units, Gardner semi-diesel 'VT' and 'T' types were also provided for marine auxiliary duties. This pair of 3T5 engines was for generating electricity.

LEFT: By the time of the outbreak of World War One, Gardner's range of engines was quite comprehensive, with simple horizontals being made alongside multi-cylinder verticals. Here is a twin-flywheel 3FS petrol fuelled single cylinder horizontal.

engines. If all the various fuelling options are considered for most of these then Gardner's were able to supply something like one hundred and fifty choices. But there was more to come before that first great upheaval of the twentieth century, the First World War.

As Thomas and Edward Gardner were changing the emphasis of their company from general engineering to specialist engine manufacturing in the 1890s, others were working on the development of compression ignition engines. Such an engine would not require a separate source of ignition. The theory was simple, but the practicalities were difficult, especially the injection of fuel into the cylinders. If petrol vapour was used from a carburettor system then

the heat of the compressed air in the cylinder would cause premature ignition, making it impossible to time the engine correctly. Consequently a heavier fuel than petrol was needed which would still be liquid when it entered the cylinder. In the year 1890 Herbert Ackroyd-Stuart patented an engine design in which fuel oil was injected into air compressed by the piston stroke. The compression ratio was not high enough to raise the air temperature sufficiently to permit spontaneous combustion of the oil when it entered the cylinder, so a separate means of ignition was still necessary.

A well-remembered German engineer, Dr. Rudolf Diesel, announced his theoretical compression ignition engine in 1892.

Horizontal designs continued to be specified with various fuelling options and this 4AF was a paraffin engine.

This outlined the principle of complete compression ignition whereby the compressed air temperature in the cylinder was high enough to ignite the fuel oil when it was sprayed into the cylinder. In 1897 Dr. Diesel was able to successfully demonstrate his theory with a working engine. Incidentally, Dr. Diesel used a blast of air to inject fuel oil into his engines and continued to do so for some time. Gardner's were never so crude, using mechanical fuel injection from the inception of their first

ABOVE: Updated versions of 'H' types were introduced in 1913, designated 'HC' engines, and heavy oil fuelled options became available. This 8HC was such an oil engine and these engines gained reputations for outstanding economy; another envied Gardner trait for decades to come. Both 'H' and 'HC' types were produced concurrently.

TOP LEFT: Occasionally Gardner's did produce more complicated horizontal types, and this twin-cylinder 10H was known as a "double" or "duplex set". It ran on producer gas.

BOTTOM LEFT: The largest Gardner horizontals were massive machines and this 11H was also a producer gas fuelled unit. Producer gas, also known as "poor gas" was made in-house by many factories as a cheaper alternative to Town Gas. Coke was heated in a firebox and pressurised steam was forced through it to, resulting in a combustible gas.

compression ignition engines. Dr. Diesel's name would eventually be universally applied to that type of engine. These early compression ignition fuel oil engines bore little or no resemblance to those of the type everyone is familiar with today. In comparison they were rudimentary and slow revving, and much too big for anything other than marine or industrial uses.

However there was potentially a huge market for compression ignition engines. They would be particularly suitable for applications where continuous running at set revolutions was required, such as for electricity generation, or for ocean-going ships. The low cost of the fuel they could use was also very attractive.

It was to compression ignition engines that Gardner's next turned their attention. It is believed that some experimental engines were made to Dr. Diesel's patents, but they proved to be unsatisfactory. Gardner's decided to base their designs on those of Ackroyd-Stuart and in 1913 the first Gardner "semi-diesels" appeared. They utilised a two-stroke cycle and they were the 'T' and 'VT' types. They were a simple design with no valves and ignition was achieved by a combination of heat generated by compressing air in

End view of an 8HC showing the intricacies of its cylinder head and fuel injection equipment. The fuel sprayer is recognizable as being virtually identical to those made by specialist firms such as Simms and CAV up to 60 years after this engine was made and its photograph taken.

the cylinder and warmth retained in cylinder head antechambers. They incorporated a patented Gardner injector that rotated and sprayed fuel oil into the hottest part of the cylinder head when the engine was idling. This innovation overcame one of the failings of earlier 'hot bulb' engines which tended to stall when the revolutions dropped. This was because the antechambers cooled and part of the means of ignition was lost. To start these engines from cold the cylinder head ante-chambers had to be heated with a blowlamp. As many were marine installations, stokers used to shovelling coal into boilers were

quite happy to do this task for a few minutes. Later Gardner's perfected electrically heated glow plugs and these were fitted.

These were also very reliable engines in the Gardner tradition. They offered high power to weight ratios and they could be fuelled by either paraffin or fuel oil, which came to be known as diesel oil. They became very popular marine engines because there was no need for a reversing gear; this was simply achieved by stopping the engine and re-starting it with the two-stroke cycle reversed. A 'VT' designation was given to the range of engines that could be supplied in various

sizes with one, two, three, or four cylinders. In total there were twenty-one versions. Power outputs ranged from a single cylinder '2VT' producing 3.5 bhp at 500 rpm, to a four-cylinder '4/8VT' with an output of 120 bhp at 290 rpm. The first of all the "semi-diesels", 4VT/17534 was tested on 13th June 1913. 'T' types were all multiple cylinder engines of either, two, three, four, or six cylinders and there were sixteen different options listed. Power outputs were between 36 bhp at 450 rpm (a '3T4') and 300 bhp at 290 rpm, which was a '6T9' and the biggest available.

Following the successful intro-

duction of their two-stroke semi-diesel design, Gardner's introduced an updated range of four-stroke horizontal engines, based on their 'H' types. These were designated 'HC' and the first one was tested on 27th August 1913. They gained a reputation for economy, another admirable Gardner trait, which would become recognised for posterity. The 'HC' types complemented 'H' engines, which remained in production.

With all the engine development taking place in the first years at Barton Hall it would have been understandable if other aspects of the business had suffered.

A couple of close ups of a 4-cylinder 'T' type semi-diesel showing the details of the engine. This was precision engineering of the highest quality and Gardner's at Barton Hall made every component and pipe. There were many man-hours needed to assemble these engines and one skilled engineer was responsible for building an individual engine, a tradition that was to last until the 1990s.

TOP LEFT: This was a 4VT semi-diesel for driving a W.H. Allen & Sons Ltd. dynamo, which in turn is turning a radiator fan. This arrangement was probably for demonstration purposes, as it does seem to be rather an unusual set-up.

BOTTOM LEFT: There were many different applications for Gardner engines and this 2/4VT was designed to drive a gearbox and separate pump from the front of its crankshaft, rather than from the more usual flywheel end. Almost certainly this was for a marine installation.

TOP RIGHT: Gardner 'T' series engines took the company into the larger marine, main propulsion market, but there were also some big marine auxiliary units. This 4T5 was for driving a pump, compressor, and alternator. The mounting plinth alone must have weighed a couple of tons and this was cast in the Patricroft foundry.

BOTTOM RIGHT: The largest 'T' type marine main propulsion engine was a 6T9 producing 300 bhp at 290 rpm. Not much smaller was this 6T8 unit and the crankshafts for these biggest Gardner engines were made in two sections and bolted together.

ABOVE: An early view of the foundry at Barton Hall that was able to cast ferrous, bronze, and later aluminium alloy components. It enabled Gardner's to maintain their high standards of quality at every stage of the production process. For much of its existence the foundry was labour intensive, but this mainly coincided with periods when manpower was plentiful.

TOP RIGHT: Another early picture of the pattern shop where skilled craftsmen first made all 'mock-up' engine components in wood. Note the line shafting for driving some of the bigger lathes and machinery at the far end of the building.

BOTTOM RIGHT: The fitting shop photographed at the same time as the foundry and pattern shop. In this picture are over 30 men and women, with the few women visible working in the stores area behind the mesh screen. Because of the presence of women, this and other pictorial evidence suggests these factory photographs were taken during the First World War.

Fortunately Gardner's had the offices of Norris and Henty to look after sales, advertising and what today is termed marketing. This relationship was further cemented in the year 1906 when Gardner's bought Norris and Henty. The agency was re-named Norris, Henty, & Gardners Ltd., but it was a separate company capitalised at £31,000. Edward Norris, who had been appointed to Gardner's Board of Directors in 1903, was Chairman of the new company. His fellow Directors were George Henty, Thomas Gardner, and Harry Grove, who was an employee of the former organisation. Sadly, Mr Grove had problems with alcohol and was asked to resign. Norris and Henty decided to sell their firm to Gardner's because they had no family to continue the business.

ABOVE: From the earliest days of engine production it was Gardner's policy to run every engine made at Barton Hall. This was the engine testing bay and in view is a large horizontal, various sizes of 'V' and 'VT' types, and probably an 'M' type. The testing bay was equipped with an overhead, travelling crane, and it must have been a noisy place to be if all the engines were running together!

TOP RIGHT: For the first 35 years of internal combustion engine production Gardner's rarely deleted an engine type from its catalogue. Very early designs were updated, but even if a customer ordered one of the originals many years later, the company would make it, especially in the difficult years of the 1920s when any order was very welcome. This 1AV marine auxiliary set comprising a dynamo and pump was made some 17 years after the first of its kind appeared.

BOTTOM RIGHT: Marine auxiliary engines were often multi-functional sets and this 2BCR petrol unit powered a compressor, generated electricity from a dynamo, and drove a couple of pumps.

TOP LEFT: A Gardner 3T6 marine propulsion unit with compressor and pump. These semi-diesels established the Patricroft firm as an important supplier of marine engines for a variety of inshore craft such as ferries, small coasters, and fishing vessels.

BOTTOM LEFT: This 4T6 had to work hard for its living with a massive flywheel, large dynamo, pump, and compressor. It was a Trinity House lighthouse generating set and the air compressor was for the foghorn. Two engines were supplied to each lighthouse to ensure it was never inoperative. Such engines as 'T' types were started from cold by using stored compressed air to turn the flywheel and by heating the antechambers with blowlamps until sufficient heat and momentum had been gained for them to run unaided.

Other prominent Directors of Norris, Henty & Gardners Ltd. in later years included Joseph and Edward Gardner, Gordon Houghton, and D.M. Denholm. New offices for the company were acquired at 115, Queen Victoria Street in the City of London, and this was known as "Gardner House".

Even though Gardner's owned Norris, Henty, & Gardners Ltd. they had little influence on its affairs. With the exception of one or two anomalies all engine sales were through Norris, Henty & Gardners and they bought them from Barton Hall at a maximum discount of 45% off list price. All orders were placed with London office that then advised Barton Hall Works of its requirements. One or two export customers who pre-dated the original 1891 association between Gardner's and Norris and Henty were allowed to purchase directly from the factory. In particular a French concern called LeCombe had imported Robinson Hot Engines, then early Gardner horizontals and dynamos, so they were permitted to continue with this arrangement. Other overseas clients who dealt exclusively with Barton Hall Works were Dumoulin – Nagant, Wynmalen & Hausmann, and Eduard Goedicke. All were given a maximum 30% discount off listed prices. Apart

from these Norris, Henty, & Gardners Ltd. handled all other exports of Gardner products through an appointed network of agents overseas. One other English customer allowed to trade directly with Gardner's was Harold Smith whose firm later made excavators. He was given 40% discount terms.

Obviously the tremendous growth of Gardner's in the early twentieth century had other implications. In the fifteen years since the move to Barton Hall in 1898 to 1913 the labour force increased tenfold, from 100 employees to over 1,000. All these additional workers had to be recruited and trained for manufacturing engines, which then was frontier-breaking technology. It was a magnificent achievement by all concerned that the company prospered in the way it did and established an envied reputation for its products. It was a time of continuous activity; expansion of the product range, expansion of Barton Hall Works, and expansion of the workforce.

The Gardner family was enlightened enough to consider the welfare of their employees. A large canteen was built and with plenty of spare land available at Barton Hall recreational facilities were

provided. Clubs were formed for soccer, cricket, and lacrosse, and pitches were laid down. There were tennis courts, a bowling green, and a rifle range. For less sports minded and older workers there was a reading room, and a social club that hosted meetings of orchestral and dramatic societies. The Gardner brothers prided themselves on the feeling still of a "family firm", although they governed an enterprise that was a public company. Sir Kenneth Crossley, a business rival and prominent Manchester businessman wrote to the Directors inviting Gardner's to join the Industrial Welfare Society. This organisation championed the welfare of employees and encouraged employers to provide better conditions for their staff. Sir Kenneth was an active supporter of these aims. The Gardner brothers declined the invitation because they believed the working conditions they provided, along with recreational facilities, far surpassed those of most other similar factories and companies.

As the company expanded Gardner's promoted from within to fill the supervisory and management positions required. Most of these appointments were made to long serving employees and Gardner's were noted as a firm where sons followed fathers, and brothers and cousins worked alongside one another. H.E. Hunter first filled the important position of Works Manager at Barton Hall, and in due course some of his successors were appointed to the Board of Directors. Reporting to him were foremen, charge hands, and inspectors. The latter fulfilled the quality control function and there were "specialists" whose job it was to investigate and rectify incidences of sub-standard

Not only did 'T' series engines generate electricity and propel marine craft, they also drove machinery in factories. In this picture a 4-cylinder 'T' type, (far right), was used to drive line shafting, which in turn supplied the motive power for spinning frames.

work. Skilled fitters assembled the engines and it was Gardner's policy to have one man for each engine made.

When the youngest Gardner brother, William, became twenty-one years of age he joined the Board of Directors and received a shareholding. All the brothers shared in the day-to-day management of the company with specific responsibilities. Ernest oversaw administration matters aided by William. Lawrence, being disabled, worked mainly in specially constructed workshops at home, where he made precision parts and prototype components

for engines under development. Thomas was Chairman of the company. He and Edward were in charge of design and development, and Joseph organised the factory. He was responsible for commissioning the new foundry, and then developed a range of machine tools before becoming joint chief designer. All the brothers were Directors but titles meant nothing to them. They were simply the proprietors of a family firm. Obviously, with L. Gardner & Sons Ltd. being a public company they had certain legal obligations. But it was a business they derived enormous satisfaction from. There

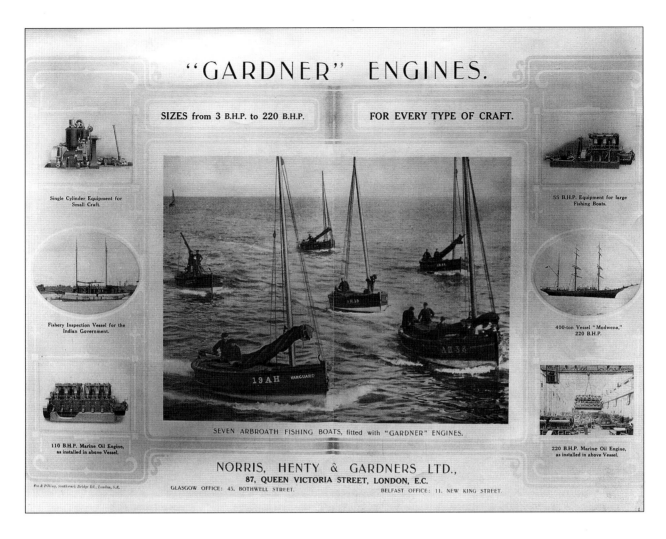

"GARDNER" ENGINES.

SIZES from 3 B.H.P. to 220 B.H.P.   FOR EVERY TYPE OF CRAFT.

Single Cylinder Equipment for Small Craft.

Fishery Inspection Vessel for the Indian Government.

110 B.H.P. Marine Oil Engine, as installed in above Vessel.

55 B.H.P. Equipment for large Fishing Boats.

400-ton Vessel "Modwena," 220 B.H.P.

220 B.H.P. Marine Oil Engine, as installed in above Vessel.

SEVEN ARBROATH FISHING BOATS, fitted with "GARDNER" ENGINES.

NORRIS, HENTY & GARDNERS LTD.,
87, QUEEN VICTORIA STREET, LONDON, E.C.
GLASGOW OFFICE: 45, BOTHWELL STREET.   BELFAST OFFICE: 11, NEW KING STREET.

were no personal extravagances displayed by any of them. Profits were ploughed back into the business to fund the next range of engines, or provide more buildings and machinery at Barton Hall. This policy paid off handsomely and within ten years of becoming a public company the value of the shares had quadrupled.

None of the Gardner Brothers devoted much time to public service, they were simply too busy with their firm. Thomas was a Justice of the Peace and served for six years on Eccles Town Council between 1906 and 1912. He was a member of the Electricity Committee, and no

doubt gained plenty of enjoyment in this role by helping set up the town's electricity supply.

Whether Thomas Gardner was at all apprehensive back in 1890 when he assumed responsibility for the business is not known. If he was, then within a few years all his doubts must have dissipated. With the help of his brothers he transformed the company in less than twenty-five years. In size, type and range of products the growth achieved was outstanding. Yet in many ways it was just a foretaste of what lay ahead. The next twenty-five years would see Gardner's rise to even greater heights.

This is a photographic copy of an advertisement that Norris, Henty & Gardners Ltd. placed with "FISHING NEWS" on 2nd January 1914. Interestingly the original advert appeared in colour, – black, green and buff. The first edition of this journal was published in 1913, with the Patricroft company being only the second engine manufacturer to advertise in it, in October 1913. Gardner's were still using the magazine over 50 years later.

CHAPTER

4

TROUBLED TIMES

When gathering storm clouds of war finally engulfed Europe in conflict they heralded a period of change at Gardner's. Not surprisingly the early weeks of confrontation caused much uncertainty, and short-time working had to be introduced at Barton Hall. The government had no contingency plans for munitions production and it was ill prepared for mechanised land battles. As was befitting a great naval power, the Royal Navy was modernising its dreadnoughts and battle cruisers, but most of these would prove to be superfluous in the months and years to come.

Approximately one hundred Gardner's employees enlisted into the armed forces on the outbreak of war. By October 1914 full time working was re-instated as the company started to manufacture carriages for Vickers 18 pounder guns. Other armament production soon followed and by spring 1915, additional workers were desperately needed. Barton Hall Works came under government control and an order was placed for the machining of 10,000 shell casings, along with some other similar work.

The need for additional employees was becoming crucial because long serving men were leaving Gardner's to join the forces. So, a decision was taken to recruit women onto the shop floor. With today's emphasis on sexual equality and political correctness it might be necessary to remind readers that working conditions for women were very different in 1915. Those who were married tended to stay at home with their children and those

This view of the crank bay at Barton Hall was taken in 1917 when Gardner TS tank engines were being produced to the design of Harry Ricardo, the leading British engine expert of the time. This doesn't appear to have been the tidiest department at the works and several completed crankshafts are visible at the far end of the department.

in employment were probably either single or widowed. Northern textile mills employed girls and women, but domestic service, nursing, and retailing were the customary careers available to females. There were minimal numbers of female office workers and virtually none at all in heavy industry and engineering.

To the credit of the Gardner brothers and their managers they handled the recruitment and induction of women employees well. Initial instruction and training was given in evenings after the men had finished for the day. To begin with the first women recruits assembled in the works offices before going to their workstations en masse. As their numbers increased it became impractical to do this. The women were provided with seating at their machines and they were allowed an afternoon tea break period, during which they were served tea and biscuits. Their working day was five minutes shorter than that of the men.

Two views of TS tank engines in production in 1917 with the stages of building these engines on display. They were massive, 6-cylinder petrol engines and by the end of hostilities capable of an output of 225 bhp. The battle tank was one of the main technological innovations of World War One, (another was the use of aeroplanes), and Gardner's assembled 250 TS units, one quarter of the total made. They also made all the crankshafts for the other appointed tank engine manufacturers.

LIST OF

TRADE **BOREAS** MARK

Patent Air Compressors.

CLASS **Y** TYPE.

PHOTO OF PETROL-DRIVEN COMPRESSOR. SIZE 4Y.

GARDNER 1BM

LACY = HULBERT & CO.

LIMITED,

Pneumatic Engineers,

25, VICTORIA ST., WESTMINSTER, LONDON, S.W.

Boreas Works, BEDDINGTON, SURREY.

Telegrams: "PERCUSSIVE, LONDON."   Telephone: 944 VICTORIA.

ALL COMMUNICATIONS TO BE ADDRESSED TO LONDON OFFICE.

LEFT: In the years leading up to World War One Gardner's had established good levels of business with Lacy-Hulbert & Co. Ltd., who made a range of air compressors under the "Boreas" trade mark. Gardner's supplied various engines for powering these compressors, with the size of engine determined by the capacity of compressed air required. This was the front cover of a catalogue printed in 1912 and features a Size 4Y compressor which was driven by a Gardner 1BM engine.

BELOW: A letterhead from the 1910s decade proclaiming that the firm was "On Admiralty, War, and India Office Lists". The codes referred to are those shown in Chapter 3 for identifying engines and was a publication listing every user of the system.

TOP RIGHT: The manufacture of crank pin turning machines was more than a sideline for Gardner's in the first couple of decades of the twentieth century; it was an important part of their business. Joseph Gardner designed these machines, originally for their own use, but 231 were also sold to other engine manufacturers at home and abroad. Many famous names bought them including Rolls Royce, Daimler, Sunbeam, Austin, Wolseley, Lanchester, Rover, and Vauxhall. The largest were known as 30 inches machines, as shown in the photograph, driven by a 20 bhp electric motor turning at 300/1200 rpm.

BOTTOM RIGHT: Various sizes of Gardner crank pin turning machines being assembled at the works. In true Gardner fashion these were extremely well made and some were still being used at Barton Hall over 50 years later. In addition to automotive engine makers, industrial and marine engine manufacturers such as Peter Brotherhood, Ruston & Hornsby, and Dorman also bought them.

RIGHT: This was a battery of 22 inches crank pin turning machines being used in 1917 at Patricroft to produce TS tank engine crankshafts, some of which are shown in the foreground. These machines could either be driven by individual electric motors, or with belts from overhead line shafts.

BELOW: Labour shortages during the First World War caused women to be employed in engineering work for the first time, and Gardner's employed some 240 females by the end of 1917, some 25% of the workforce at Patricroft. In this picture one of the women employees was seen minding a crankpin turning machine and she was wearing the uniform provided by the company.

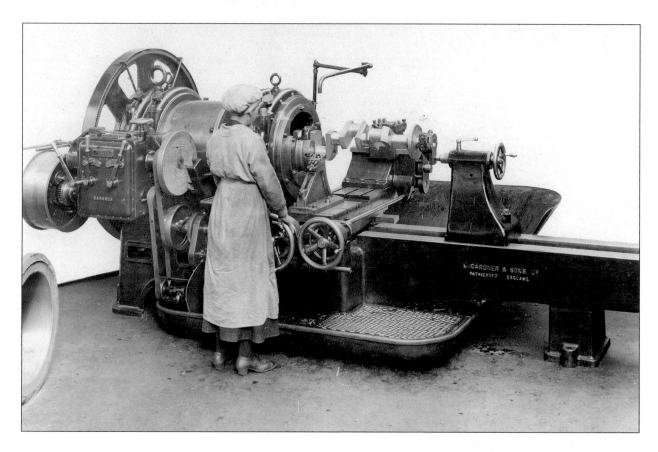

L. GARDNER & SONS LIMITED

Those supervising the women on the shop floor, – their instructors and foremen, – were in something of a dilemma at first. Unsure of how to manage women and girls, they decided to treat them as young male apprentices. This worked perfectly and was a satisfactory solution. The Works Manager of the time, Mr. Hunter, suggested that the new recruits be provided with suitable working garments. A serviceable and practical black overall evolved, which being rather tight fitting, kept ordinary clothing such as skirts away from unguarded driving belts and gears. A white collar gave the overall a feminine touch. These female employees were fully integrated into the Gardner "family firm" and allowed access to sports and recreational facilities. Sometimes this had an adverse effect, with for instance, dancing becoming more popular than athletics. The standard of tennis playing also fell, to such an extent that Gardner's hired a professional coach to try and improve the girls' games!

By the end of 1917 Gardner's employed 240 women and girls out of a total workforce of 943 people. Within a few more months the number of females climbed to 320, and just a few weeks before the Armistice a decision was made to employ women in the foundry moulding shop.

Alongside armaments production, engines were still being built. In 1915 and 1916 demand for the normal Gardner range was still good. Interestingly a Gardner powered generating set for searchlights was in demand as firstly Zeppelins, and then aircraft were used increasingly during the course of the war. This particular searchlight design is believed to have been very similar to one introduced as early as 1906, only a couple of years or so after the first internal combustion engined aeroplane flight by Orville and Wilbur Wright in December 1903.

The battle tank was perfected during the First World War and Gardner's was one of a select few companies chosen to produce power units. The War Office had investigated this concept of an armoured fighting vehicle for the first time in 1909. Referred to as "landships", the name 'tank' had stuck. Early ones were based on motorised gun tractors with the principal object being an ability to cross trenches. Some of the best civilian engineers were involved and a great many designs were tried with varying success. Eventually the now familiar World War One lozenge shaped battle tank evolved, type Mark V.

There was only one type of petrol engine used for World War I tanks and it was designed by Harry (later Sir Harry) Ricardo, who was an eminent engineer. Gardner's designated their tank engine as type 'TS', and at first these produced 150 bhp at 1,250 rpm. Barton Hall was also responsible for making every tank engine crankshaft for the other manufacturers. Gardner's supplied over 250 battle tank engines, some of which were uprated to 225 bhp. When output reached its peak, from the latter months of 1917, they were building ten power units weekly. Being a somewhat extravagant design they were invoiced at £500 each, well above the norm at that time. In total 1,004 tank engines were made during the war by Gardner's, armament specialists, vehicle builders, and locomotive works. Gardner's also designed a tank engine test-bed, capable of tilting to 45 degrees in every plane.

All Gardner crankshafts were turned on machines designed by Joseph Gardner and made in-house. They permitted crankshafts to be machined to extremely fine tolerances and were so successful that Gardner's established a thriving machine tool business. Virtually every engine maker in the country, and many overseas, bought Gardner crankshaft machine tools. Included in the list of clients were such well-known companies as Ruston, National, Crossley, Lister, Petter, and Rolls Royce. Fifty were also exported to Russia.

Statistics for engine production at Barton Hall Works during World War I make interesting reading and are reproduced below.

ENGINE PRODUCTION 1915 to 1918

YEAR	ENGINES MADE	VALUE OF PRODUCTION	AVERAGE VALUE OF ENGINE
1915	1,136	£82,083	£72
1916	1,061	£86,239	£81
1917	699	£132,115	£189
1918	391	£154,495	£395

RIGHT: Gardner's first major development of the early 1920s was a modernisation of their larger horizontal engines. Heavy oil versions were provided with spherical combustion chambers, and pre-dated, by at least five years, a similar design introduced to great acclaim by Ricardo Engineering consultancy. This is a 5HF horizontal engine.

'HF' type oil engines were part of a development programme to produce true compression ignition, or diesel engines, that commenced in 1919. Larger engines, such as this massive 14HF shown here, were started by using compressed air to turn their flywheels. Interestingly, the plate attached above "Gardner" on the crankcase casting reads Walker & Greig Ltd., presumably another engineering concern using Gardner engines to drive machinery it supplied.

Obviously, the large six-cylinder tank engines were costly items and time consuming to manufacture, hence the increasing monetary value for fewer units produced. This was undoubtedly a policy that Gardner's would actively pursue in subsequent years.

Another engine made later in the war was significant for gaining experience of aluminium alloys. This was a lightweight six-cylinder marine unit, designed by Gardner's and supplied in 1918 to the Italian Navy for powering motor torpedo boats. Known as the '6RC' type, it was the forerunner of a distinguished line of light alloy engines in future. After the war experiments were made with aluminium alloy four-cylinder engines, but they were shelved because of the severe slump in the 1920s.

Four years of warfare brought new challenges to the Directors, managers, and employees of Gardner's. They met them all and enhanced the reputation of their company and its products. There were many difficulties to surmount, not least of these being food rationing, which was introduced in the last months of conflict. Sugar became scarce and a special war workers' allowance had to be applied for and granted. Other foodstuffs remained in short supply and some of the sports fields were ploughed and cultivated. Even the women had to forego biscuits with their afternoon tea! When the Armistice was declared on 11th November 1918 the Directors hastily convened a meeting and granted a holiday for their employees. Barton Hall Works remained closed for the rest of the week with everybody on the payroll receiving full wages.

Within days of the Armistice, Gardner's were asked to suspend much of their munitions production, and although engine manufacturing could quickly be resumed, it was a period of uncertainty. The year 1919 proved to be relatively busy for Gardner's as there was a backlog of engine orders to fulfil. As former employees returned from war service to reclaim their jobs many of the women had to be laid off, leaving only thirty-five of them to take afternoon tea. Eleven of Gardner's men made the ultimate sacrifice for their King and country, and never returned.

The company records reveal that despite 919 engines being made in 1920 with a value of £121,627, (see Appendix B), only the Barton Hall foundry was profitable. And this was only achieved by accepting work from other firms. But looking to the future, the Directors extended the foundry and installed a new overhead electric crane. This complemented their investment in a new laboratory in 1919.

For three years from 1921 to 1923 Gardner's experienced a severe and serious downturn in business. Layoffs became inevitable and there were extended factory shut downs, three day weeks, and other cutbacks. The workforce was reduced by more than half, to just 420 employees. The desperate year of 1923 saw a paltry total of 290 engines produced for a value of £34,560. This same year saw the introduction of further developments to the bigger industrial horizontal engines, although the first of these was in fact tested at the very end of 1922 on the 28th December. Now designated as 'HF' types they could still be specified to run on various fuels. Significantly, the oil versions had a spherical combustion chamber. In 1928 the Ricardo Engineering Consultancy announced to great acclaim a similar combustion chamber pattern as a vital part of the design of its Ricardo Mark I indirect fuel injection system for oil engines. Gardner's ideas pre-dated this "breakthrough" by at least five years!

The 'HF' oil engine was part of a development programme instigated in 1919 by the principals of Gardner's. Their long-term aim was to design and produce a true compression ignition engine encompassing the ideas of Dr. Diesel. Such engines would have no need for blowlamps, hot tubes, heated antechambers, or glow plugs. Smaller Gardner 'HF' engines were still hand cranked for starting, but larger versions utilised compressed air to spin their flywheels fast enough for them to fire-up. Other research brought improvements to Gardner's semi-diesel two-strokes, giving improved fuel economy and increased power. All this generation of engines were relatively slow revving and the high-speed small compression ignition engine was still some years away in the future.

By improving their engine ranges Gardner's were able to charge customers more for them, further enhancing the Gardner reputation for a premium quality product. In itself this was an unusual course of action to take in a trade depression. Normally, under such circumstances prices fall as rival manufacturers fight for their share of a decreasing or static market. Gardner's policy proved to be a success. In the nadir of 1923 their average engine value was £119. Two years later by 1925, although engine sales had only increased by 209 units, the average value had virtually doubled to £235 per engine. Despite a slight blip in 1926 (the year of the General Strike and some civil unrest), this trend

ABOVE: Registered in Shanghai, the "Shung King" was built in Kiangnan Dock for Chinese owners for service above Chungking. With an overall length of 80 feet, the vessel weighed 51 tons and was powered by twin Gardner 4T6 semi-diesel engines producing 96 bhp each. These were engine numbers 27188 & 9, and gave a speed of just over 11 knots. This photograph was taken in June 1927.

LEFT: Gardner powered ferries and other craft were common in Chinese coastal waters from the 1920s and some of the biggest engines ever produced at Barton Hall were destined for the Far East. This shot taken inside the engine room of the "Yin Hung" shows part of the twin 'T' series engines installation.

RIGHT: Gardner engines on display at the British Industries Fair held at Birmingham in 1925. The mid-twenties were a very difficult period for the firm with low sales figures. On show were a large horizontal, 70 bhp HF oil engine, a smaller horizontal 8 bhp oil unit, and in the background, a 'T' type semi-diesel. Note that the distinctive Gardner logo had emerged by that time.

BELOW RIGHT: When Gardner's introduced their first true diesel design it was a slow speed, self-reversing, marine two-stroke. This diagram of the 'J' type cylinder has been taken from a detailed brochure for these acclaimed engines.

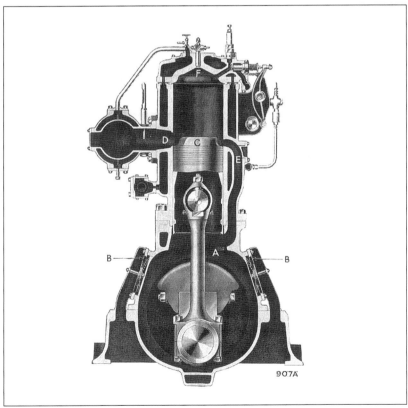

continued strongly, although annual engine sales did not match the 1925 total again until 1930. By then the average engine value had risen to £379.

For much of the 1920s only the marine engine market was reasonably buoyant. In the year 1928 Gardner's introduced a full compression ignition range designated 'J' type. This was a self-reversing two-stroke design and various 'J' types could produce between 54 and 400 bhp from configurations of between three and eight cylinders. They were started by compressed air stored in cylinders charged by the engines themselves. This was achieved by incorporating an air compressor into the forward section of the engines. For starting from cold, or emergency purposes, the air reservoirs could be re-charged by a small petrol driven compressor designated as type 'OVC'. These engines had been brought out in 1925 and were able to store 4 cubic feet of compressed air at 250 lbs. per square inch pressure in 22 minutes. The merits of 'J' types and other engines in the improved Gardner range were soon recognised and orders gradually increased. Also, an increasing percentage of Barton Hall's annual output was being fuelled by oil.

ABOVE TOP: To describe 'J' type engines as "hefty" is something of an understatement, as can be gauged by this picture of a 6-cylinder engine bed, crankshaft, and main bearings. These main marine propulsion units took Gardner's into the field of heavy engineering, but the bottom end design of J engines allowed easy access for inspection.

ABOVE: A 4J9 producing 200 bhp at 290 rpm. The column with the hand wheel was known as the governor column. It consisted of a governor control and stopping lever, a variable speed gear, a compressed air starting lever, reversing sector and pointer, and oil pressure gauge. The hand wheel was for reversing the engine and when it was turned the camshaft rotated relative to the crankshaft, which in turn placed the cams into the correct angular position for running either ahead or astern as required.

RIGHT: This view of the fore end of a 'J' type engine illustrates the 2-stage air compressor, water circulation pump, and bilge pump, all of which were supplied as part of the engine. The compressor was for charging air reservoirs and compressed air was used for starting engines from cold. To guard against accidental loss of compressed air, or for starting after overhaul or inspection, a standby, separate engine driven compressor was provided.

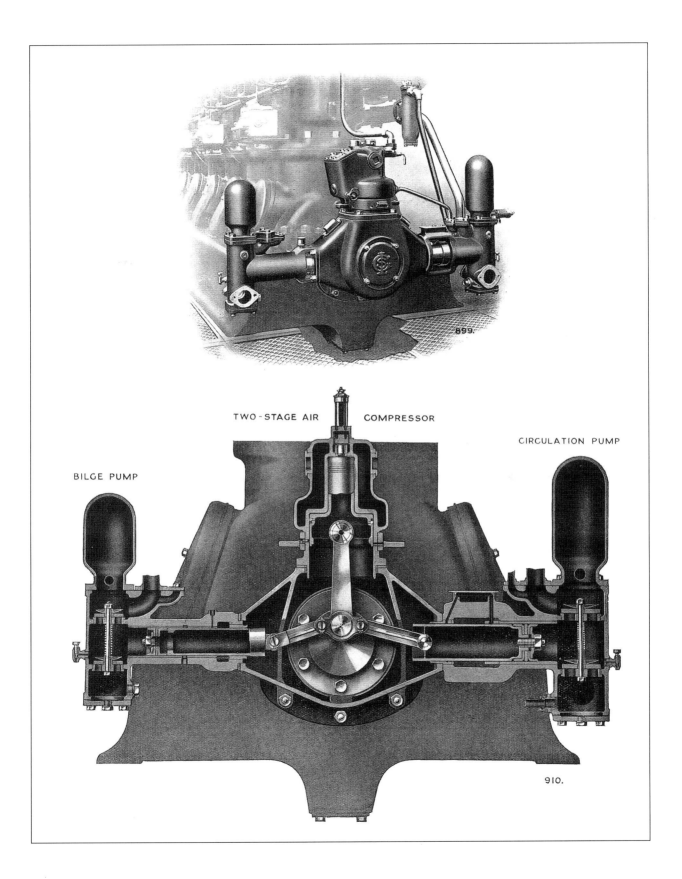

899.

BILGE PUMP

TWO-STAGE AIR COMPRESSOR

CIRCULATION PUMP

910.

TOP: *The largest engines ever produced at Barton Hall Engine Works were 8J9s, capable of producing 400 bhp at 290 rpm. The example illustrated was arranged for power transmission from both ends of the engine. The cylinder dimensions were 12½ inches bore by 15 inches stroke and the engine, with flywheel and clutch weighed 27 tons 13 hundredweights. The complete installation with air bottles and ancillary equipment was almost 33 tons. The first Gardner 8J9 was delivered in 1932 to Dodwell of Hong Kong for installing in a ferryboat.*

ABOVE: *A Sudanese river paddleboat, the "Nasir", fitted with twin Gardner 6J7 two-stroke diesel marine engines in 1937. Each unit produced 180 bhp at 340 rpm and drive to the paddlewheel was via Browns single reduction gears. 'J' type engines remained in production for a relatively short period (by Gardner's standards) of 12 years, when wartime demands in 1940 curtailed output of such massive units that were time consuming to manufacture.*

ABOVE: Mounting the flywheel of a Gardner 14HF engine at the British Industries Fair of 1929. Gardner's probably made the huge spanner for the nuts. Visible in the background is a two-stroke marine engine.

LEFT: A Gardner OVC air compressor that was usually supplied as the standby unit for marine and industrial engines started by compressed air. These special, single cylinder vertical engines were petrol fuelled and water-cooled and produced 1.25 bhp at 770 rpm. An OVC could charge to a maximum pressure of 350 lb. per square inch, but was normally regulated to charge a reservoir of 4 cubic feet capacity from zero to 250 lb. per square inch in 22 minutes.

A wonderful photo of elephant transport in Ceylon, now Sri Lanka. The packing case contained a massive Gardner 14HF engine, destined for either a tea plantation or sugar mill. In countries where transport infrastructures had yet to be developed any means possible was utilised to deliver machinery.

The sales policy for Gardner engines, as dictated by Norris, Henty, & Gardners during this very difficult decade was simple. If a customer required an engine, no matter how old its design, Gardner's would build it. Consequently engines designed thirty years previously would still be produced occasionally. The last 'H' type was tested on 25th July 1928, followed eleven months later by the final 'HC' type on 19th June 1929.

Sales representatives made their pitches to prospective customers by emphasising the potential cost savings obtainable with premium quality Gardner engines. Fuel oil in particular was cheap to purchase and such engines were far more economical to run than either gas or steam engines. One quoted example cited a Lancashire brick-works that had installed a 65 bhp Gardner engine. It cost 12 shillings a day to run and in comparison the steam engine it had replaced needed two tons of coal daily for its

boiler to raise steam, costing 55 shillings. Moreover there was no need for a fireman and his wages were 45 shillings weekly. So, on a five and a half days working week the Gardner engine saved 281 shillings, just over £14. On these figures the engine recovered its purchase cost in less than six months.

As the troubled 1920s came to a close the next generation of Gardner's were employed at Barton Hall. The grandsons of Lawrence inherited his engineering flair and skills. In particular the sons of Joseph Gardner, Hugh and John, would assist their father and uncles in ensuring that the family firm made one of the greatest automotive diesel engine breakthroughs of the twentieth century. In 1929 this was a market that Gardner's was not active in at all. Yet, by the end of the following decade all that would have changed as the company went on to achieve even more success.

The same 14HF engine arriving at its remote destination with a team of six oxen and a lorry bearing the load. Engines in such locations had prodigious working lives and there is a reasonable chance that such an engine as this could still exist in a place like Sri Lanka.

CHAPTER
5

REVOLUTIONISING ROAD TRANSPORT

After the difficult years of the mid-1920s the success of the updated Gardner range and the new 'J' type began restoring the company's fortunes. Development was continuing with the aims of producing lighter, smaller, and higher revving true 'Diesel' engines for marine auxiliary uses. Similar designs were also being pursued by several other engine companies, which believed these power units had great potential for automotive purposes. During the 1920s this had become something of a "Holy Grail" for engineers. Gardner's themselves were always striving for three goals; efficiency, reliability, and longevity. Their aim was to produce engines 10% to 15% more fuel-efficient than those of competitors.

There were many problems to overcome before such engines became practical propositions for road vehicles. They had to be reasonably light in weight, higher revving to provide a similar power output to petrol engines, and preferably able to inject atomised fuel directly into a combustion chamber that was an integral part of the cylinder head and piston. As Gardner's had proved, indirect injection with the fuel being sprayed into an antechamber was a practical solution, but this was only a halfway step to the ultimate goal. Dispensing with the antechamber was desirable for several reasons. There would be less heat loss and consequently a saving in fuel consumption. The engine would be smoother, and more efficient in its exhaust cycle and therefore cleaner. Pre-combustion air turbulence would also be improved prompting much easier starting when cold. However, if the antechamber was discarded it had to be replaced by a specially designed piston crown and cylinder head. This would permit fuel and air to be correctly mixed, but the fuel injection system would have to be capable of withstanding the force of the firing explosion. The correct and precise metering of the fuel and its atomisation into minute droplets was a difficult problem to resolve.

One possible advantage of an indirect injection system was that on the firing stroke the antechamber allowed gases to spread more evenly, giving the piston a steadier push. A direct injection engine would be subjected to a fiercer force on its piston, unless the combustion chamber was perfectly designed. Direct injection engines required very precise timing if they were to run smoothly and reasonably quietly. The timing of indirect injection engines was not quite so critical, and a well set up power unit of this type could be fairly quiet running. Incorrectly timed engines produced a distinctive "knocking" noise.

The German company Bosch was the pioneer that overcame fuel pump and injection difficulties. By 1924 it had a workable system on the market and Saurer of Aborn, Switzerland, took it up. They adapted a Bosch fuel pump to their engine design and made the first indirect injection diesel-engined commercial vehicles. Some other European makers followed but such engines were noisy, rough running, smelly, and smoky. They were also unreliable, and being expensive to maintain they consequently struggled to gain acceptance from vehicle operators. However, after the initial breakthroughs, improvements were slowly made but these engines fell well short of what was needed.

Several British commercial vehicle builders were investigating diesel engines in the late 1920s. Some chassis manufacturers bought proprietary engines from specialised suppliers such as Meadows, but all these were petrol fuelled. Even the

GARDNER

NORRIS, HENTY & GARDNERS L™

PROPRIETORS: L. GARDNER & SONS L™

INTERNAL COMBUSTION ENGINES,
MARINE INDUSTRIAL & TRANSPORT,
MARINE INSTALLATIONS.

TELEPHONES:
CENTRAL 1451 (2 LINES)
TELEGRAMS:
"NORNODESTE, CENT, LONDON".
CODES:
A.B.C. 6™ EDITION,
BENTLEY'S MARCONI,
AND WESTERN UNION.

DIRECTORS:
EDWARD H. NORRIS.
T. H. GARDNER.
JOSEPH GARDNER.
GORDON O. HOUGHTON.
D. M. DENHOLM.
E. W. L. GARDNER.

SECRETARY:
W. BAILEY.

ALSO AT
GLASGOW,   HULL,
124, ST. VINCENT STREET, C.2.   PARAGON HOUSE,
NEWCASTLE-ON-TYNE,   LIVERPOOL,
MILBURN HOUSE.   512, TOWER BUILDING.

HEAD OFFICE & REGISTERED OFFICE:
BARTON HALL ENGINE WORKS,
PATRICROFT, MANCHESTER.

GARDNER HOUSE,
115, QUEEN VICTORIA STREET,
LONDON, E.C.4.

YOUR REF.
OUR REF.   19

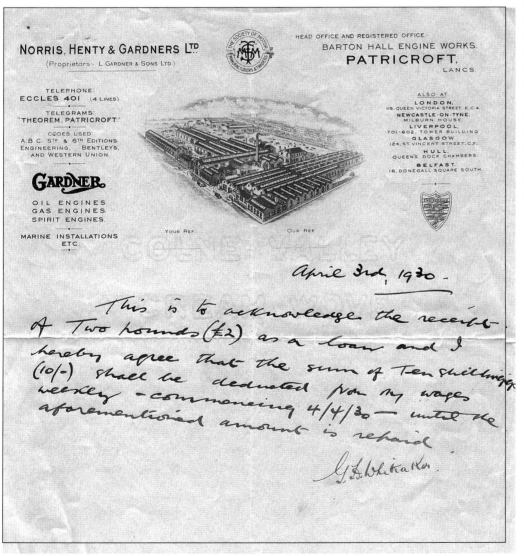

Examples of Norris, Henty & Gardners letter heads from the 1920s. The first one states the head office as Gardner House, Queen Victoria Street, London, and the other, later, example has it at Barton Hall Engine Works. An illustration of the Patricroft site was used to embellish it. This particular letterhead acknowledges the loan of £2 to an employee, repayable at 10 shillings weekly (50 pence), which in 1930 would have been a very high percentage of the individual's weekly wages.

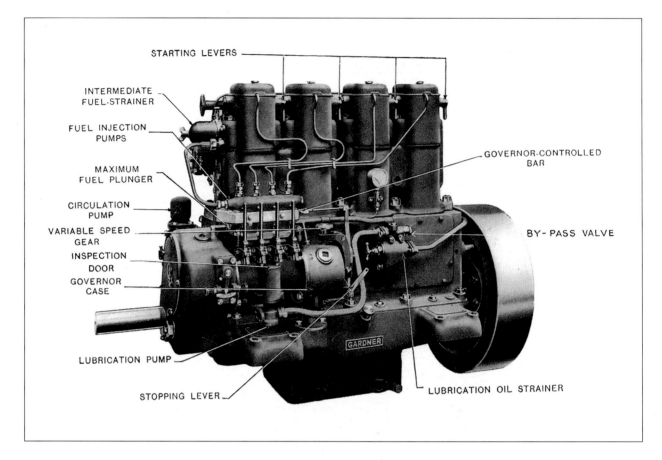

STARTING LEVERS

INTERMEDIATE
FUEL-STRAINER

FUEL INJECTION
PUMPS

MAXIMUM
FUEL PLUNGER

CIRCULATION
PUMP

VARIABLE SPEED
GEAR

INSPECTION
DOOR

GOVERNOR
CASE

LUBRICATION PUMP

STOPPING LEVER

GOVERNOR-CONTROLLED
BAR

BY-PASS VALVE

LUBRICATION OIL STRAINER

GARDNER

Gardner's L2 design was intended for marine main propulsion and marine auxiliary duties so it had certain features necessary for complying with Board of Trade regulations, as evident in this illustration with the main aspects highlighted. L2 engines had individual cylinder heads and a useful attribute with this range, (and also LW engines) was the "starting levers". These were decompression levers used to lower the compression ratio of the cylinders to facilitate easier turning over of the engine with a starting handle. When it was turning freely, because of momentum imparted by the flywheel, full compression was restored and the engine fired-up.

smaller Gardner multi-cylinder petrol types were unsuitable for automotive purposes, and their "oil" engines were much too heavy and slow revving for such applications.

Of the leading British companies Leyland Motors had a prototype diesel engine running in 1927, but it was too harsh, noisy, and rough to become a saleable proposition. It was a useful test bed for research. By December 1928, the Associated Equipment Company of Southall (AEC) had produced a six-cylinder diesel unit and they had sufficient confidence to install it into one of their own works buses. This vehicle could carry just over one hundred passengers and transported them from Walthamstow, the original location of AEC, to their new plant at Southall. Both AEC and Leyland,

two of the leading premium chassis manufacturers, were still a few years away from producing commercially viable diesel engines in spite of having prototypes running in the late 1920s.

Apart from the technical challenges of designing a satisfactory diesel engine the attraction for both vehicle builders and operators was in reducing running costs. Diesel fuel oil then was about one third the price of petrol and hard as it is to believe today, it was just two pence a gallon! In addition theoretical calculations indicated that a diesel engine would return more miles per gallon than a petrol unit of similar size. The manufacturing cost of a diesel engine was greater because it had to be more robustly made, resulting in a higher selling price. But this was sure to be offset by its far longer service life, by virtue of its lower crankshaft revolutions, and substantial savings in fuel during the same period.

It must have been a huge surprise to internal combustion engine experts when in the year 1929 Gardner's announced a new type of engine which boasted direct fuel injection. It embodied all the ideas for diesel propulsion so actively being sought. What was truly remarkable about the Gardner L2 series, as it was designated, was the fact it was a direct injection design and this was the first in the world of its size. Automotive diesel engine makers were still a few years away from achieving direct fuel injection and they utilised indirect injection systems, often relying on licensing agreements with Ricardo Engineering. If Gardner's initial breakthrough occurred in 1894 with their first internal combustion engine, then undoubtedly their second great advance was the L2 design.

To reiterate. Indirect fuel injection is when diesel fuel is injected under high pressure into a spherical chamber within the cylinder head. The compression stroke of the piston forces air, which rapidly heats up, to swirl inside the chamber. This combines with atomised particles of fuel resulting in combustion. With a direct inject-ion system pressurised droplets of fuel are injected directly into the combustion chamber after the air has been compressed almost to its maximum by the piston. The timing sequence for the fuel is critical (e.g. 30 degrees before top dead centre) and again the heated air ignites the fuel to give combustion. The combustion chamber is not in the cylinder head as such, but it is

formed by machining a bowl, or cavity, in the piston crown. For direct injection to succeed the design of the piston crown is vital and accurate timing coupled with precise fuel measurement is essential. The rewards are greater engine efficiency and better fuel economy. Gardner's achieved the "Holy Grail" by a combination of their own brilliant design of piston crown combustion chamber, precision made multi-hole fuel injectors (or "sprayers" in Gardner parlance), and a fuel injection pump combining their own cambox with a Bosch/CAV jerk pump. (C.A. Vandervell – CAV – held the British licensing agreement with Bosch for their fuel pump design).

The initial design parameters for the L2 engine range were to produce a multi-cylinder high-speed diesel to run at 1,000 rpm for marine and generating duties. Gardner's were supplying large, slower revving, marine engines for expensive luxury yachts built by boatyards such as Camper & Nicholson and J.I. Thornycroft. There was a demand for a smaller auxiliary engine for pumping, generating, and air compressing capable of running on the same kind of fuel as the main engine. Thomas Gardner, by then in his late sixties, was the firm's chief designer and it is fairly certain that he had some input into the L2 design. The main credit for this engine has always been attributed to Joseph Gardner and his sons Hugh, and John.

Before a satisfactory L2 prototype emerged it is recorded that a couple of research engines designed as two-strokes were tested. The original unit was built in 1925, followed by a smaller engine in 1928. What did finally appear was a direct injection four-stroke diesel

and it cannot be emphasised too much what an important break-through this was.

The basic design of the L2 range was for installation as marine main propulsion, and marine auxiliary engines. Cast iron construction was used and there were two styles of crankcase. One had supports to enable the engine to be mounted on bearers in the boat hull, and the other had a flat bottom to sit on a prepared base. For maintenance purposes the cylinder heads were detachable from the block, which in turn was cast separately from the upper crankcase and could be removed. With the upper crankcase removed the crankshaft became exposed and by using special tools the pistons and connecting rods could be removed from above, leaving the crankshaft in situ in the bottom crankcase, which was on the lower deck of the boat. It was also possible to inspect the main bearings and big ends without dismantling the engine. There were removable access plates on the upper crankcase and it was a Board of Trade regulation that the engine bearings of all passenger craft must be inspected annually.

A Gardner L2 engine had no resemblance to anything previously made at Barton Hall. It was a totally clean sheet design. The cylinder capacity was 1.4 litres, with a bore of 4¼ inches and stoke of 6 inches. Initially, the original intention was for a maximum governed speed of 1,000 rpm and an output of 9.5 bhp per cylinder. Soon, events decreed that L2 engines would be faster and more powerful. The very early engines had a saucer shaped combustion chamber in the piston crown, but the design was modified and improved to become a hemispherical bowl. The Gardner

Trevor Barton of Barton Transport, Nottingham spotted the potential for "oil-engined" commercial vehicles after seeing Gardner's revolutionary 4L2 engine exhibited at Olympia in August 1929. By showing groundbreaking perspicacity he installed such an engine in a Lancia single decker in 1930 and it was the first direct injection diesel powered bus to enter revenue-earning service in the world. This historic vehicle was adorned with the slogan "Barton's British Crude Oil Bus", rather an unfortunate marketing term given the connotations with the word "Crude". This term was soon dropped in favour of "oil engine", (used by Gardner's for many years), and generally "diesel engine" became the common name in the second half of the twentieth century.

sprayers were a multi-hole type with four orifices that injected fuel oil horizontally into the cylinder. Once again this was pioneering engineering of the highest quality. It would be another five years at least before competitors introduced multi-hole injectors. They persevered with single hole designs, blaming variable diesel fuel quality and poor filtration for their perceived reluctance to embrace multi-hole injectors. Maybe they did not possess the technology and skills of Gardner's and were unable to make them.

The tradition of various cylinder configurations was maintained and Gardner's offered L2 engines with between one and six cylinders. Blocks and crankcases were cast for either two or three pistons and individual cylinder heads were fitted. The 1L2 version had its own

crankcase. There was forced lubrication to all moving parts and these engines idled at 250 rpm. Normally they had heavy flywheels fitted for hand cranking, but later engines could be equipped for electric starting. They were lighter in weight per unit than any previous Gardner design. This was a significant and important feature. The prototype was a 4L2, (four-cylinder) engine number 28203, and it was tested in June 1929. It was rated for a power output of 38 bhp at 1,000 rpm.

This original 4L2 engine was exhibited at the Engineering and Marine Exhibition at Olympia in August 1929. Competing for the attention of visitors in the market category targeted by Gardner's were two other new marine engine designs from Gleniffer and Ailsa

Craig. Both were indirect injection types. The Glennifer engine was biggest and heaviest of the trio and it had clerestory style cylinder heads housing horizontally opposed valves. It remained purely a marine engine, was reasonably successful and stayed in production until the mid-1960s. The Ailsa Craig unit was described as being "hastily designed with strong spark-ignition affinities and a not very satisfactory German Acro-combustion system". (Source: 'GAS & OIL POWER'). It proved to be unsatisfactory.

Gardner's new engine attracted plenty interest but only three firm orders were received. Engine numbers 28421 & 2 were destined for marine auxiliary duties as generators. The third order came from a surprising source, one Trevor Barton, of Barton Transport of Beeston, Nottingham. Trevor Barton was a man of vision and foresaw the potential of this kind of diesel engine for automotive applications. He followed up his initial enquiry with a visit to Barton Hall Works and persuaded Gardner's to uprate a 4L2 to a maximum power output of 50 bhp at 1,300 rpm. Barton's plan was to install his engine into a Lancia single deck bus and this historic power unit; serial number 28423 was completed and tested on 28th February 1930. Officially, it is recorded as the first production Gardner L2 engine and was completed three days before the preceding two marine auxiliary sets. The exhibition engine was installed in the Barton Hall Works power-house, where it was still going strong over forty years later! For much of its existence the Gardner works was supplied with electricity generated on site. Not only was this cheaper than purchasing it from the national grid, it gave Gardner's

every opportunity of testing and evaluating engines over a considerable period of time.

After initial trials the Gardner powered Lancia bus entered revenue-earning service and it proved to be twice as economical as the petrol engine it replaced. After covering 50,000 miles in eleven months the 4L2 was removed from the Lancia and returned to Gardner's for inspection. There were no problems at all with the engine so it was reassembled and on 26th

TOP: The Pagefield lorry chassis fitted with a Gardner 4L2 engine ready for its evaluation on Parbold Hill, in Lancashire. Things were certainly done differently in September 1930, with no protection for the driver and a very insecure looking load.

ABOVE: When the test runs were carried out with the 4L2 powered Pagefield they were keenly watched by Thomas Gardner (left with pipe), Mr. Parkinson of Walker Brothers (centre), and Joseph Gardner.

RIGHT: By June 1930 Dutsons of Leeds had fitted the fifteenth Gardner 4L2 engine produced into a solid tyred Leyland, replacing its original petrol unit. Plenty of publicity was generated, extolling the cost saving merits of 'crude oil'. It was stated that 12 mpg was being obtained, costing 4.5 pennies a gallon for diesel (2p), and with a payload of 6.5 tons.

BELOW: Another early replacement of a petrol engine by a diesel unit was carried out with this Tilling Stevens six-wheeler van operated by the famous preserves makers, Chivers & Sons Ltd. of Cambridge. This was a Gardner 5L2 unit.

February 1931 it was sold to Northern Motor Utilities for fitting into a lorry. Incidentally, marine L2 engines had ram-type water circulating pumps while automotive units had centrifugal water pumps. With the precedent established, the 1,300 rpm limit was set for road going engines, with a power output of 12.25 bhp per cylinder. For continuous duty in marine and industrial applications the maximum limit was kept at 1,000 rpm.

There have been many claims and counter claims as to what company achieved "firsts" in terms of installations, and operations of diesel engined vehicles in Great Britain. With so much experimentation taking place in 1930 throughout the industry it is difficult to date precisely just who achieved what. Suffice it to say that Gardner's were definitely pioneering applications of diesel engines in road going vehicles. However, it can

be categorically stated that the Barton Lancia was the first direct injection diesel engined passenger carrying vehicle to run in Great Britain, and probably the world. This was a magnificent achievement and one to be proud of.

By no means were all the early Gardner L2 engines destined for road vehicles. Luxury yacht builders ordered several and others were used for more mundane marine applications. Industrial versions were also sold. The pioneering commercial vehicle applications are recorded as follows, along with other important installations.

On 2nd June 1930, the fifteenth 4L2, (number 28560), was supplied to Frank H. Dutson Ltd. of Leeds for fitting into a Leyland lorry. Shortly afterwards Dutson's Workshop Manager, T.H. Parkinson, became rolling-stock Manager for Leeds City Transport and the ninth 6L2 to be made, (engine number 28686), was

All kinds of lorries were converted to diesel power, but very few could surely have been as ancient and decrepit as this Maudslay, owned by Manchester provision merchants T. Seymour Mead & Co. Ltd. Even its solid rubber tyres had seen better days, but some concessions to modernity had been made, apart from its Gardner 4L2 engine, by providing new electric headlamps.

supplied to this transport undertaking on 21st August 1930. It produced 75 bhp at 1,300 rpm and was installed in a Crossley Condor double deck bus. Leeds City Transport's Fleet Number 64 was claimed to be the first diesel powered, all British passenger vehicle to enter service with a municipal authority.

The first five-cylinder 5L2 was tested on 29th April 1930 and this

Gardner's own works transport lorry loaded with LW engines. The rearmost engine is missing its rocker covers, so it had probably been put on the lorry to make a full load for the photographer. Again, the merits of diesel propulsion are extolled on the cab sides. The make of vehicle is unrecorded, but it has some modern features for its time, such as the tapered rear chassis, and rear hub design.

was for auxiliary generating duties in a yacht. The third 5L2, (number 28585), was purchased by Barton Transport on 10th June 1930. It produced 62 bhp at 1,300 rpm. The seventh 5L2 built, (number 28831), was supplied to Eastern Roadways for fitting into an AEC lorry.

A six-cylinder 6L2 version first appeared on 31st March 1930. This was serial number 28463 and was installed as the main propulsion engine in a yacht. The fifth 6L2, (number 28566), was again a notable first for Gardner's, it being sold to

Hudswell Clarke of Leeds for driving a shunting locomotive. This sale opened up the rail traction market, which would become another important outlet for the company's products.

The twelfth 6L2 went to Karrier Motors of Huddersfield on 8th September 1930. This engine, number 28704, was for a goods vehicle. Another passenger vehicle installation was the fate of the thirteenth 6L2, (serial number 28722). It went to Sheffield Corporation Transport on 12th September 1930 and was fitted into a Crossley bus. One of Gardner's local bus operators, Manchester Corporation Transport, purchased the eighteenth 6L2, (number 28778), on 17th October 1930. It too was installed into a Crossley, which was the most common make in that fleet.

Single cylinder 1L2s were only supplied commercially for industrial applications and generating. The first was number 28762 and it also made its debut in 1930. Because of the efficiency of the L2 concept several 1L2s were bought by oil companies

and technical colleges as standard test engines. The earliest 2L2 was number 28451, which was tested on 20th March 1930. Installed as a generator in the yacht *"Kiloran"* it was known to be still in service forty years later in 1970. Following on from this 2L2, on the next day 21st March 1930, the original 3L2 appeared. It was number 28414 and powered a Wallis & Stevens road roller.

Following the success of Gardner L2 installations several of the smaller commercial vehicles manufacturers offered them as original equipment. Tilling Stevens Motors listed the 4L2 engine in a dual-purpose chassis that could be bodied either as a bus or lorry. Peerless Lorries and Parts specified this same power unit as an optional fitting in their lorries and Karrier produced a heavy goods model with a Gardner 6L2. There was also a Wigan based company, Walker Brothers, which made Pagefield lorries and 4L2 engines were fitted in them. Walker's used the local Parbold Hill for evaluation and testing purposes. At its steepest this

LEFT: Pagefield lorries were well designed and competed with the likes of Leyland and AEC. Being made in small numbers they were expensive and Walker Brothers eventually decided to concentrate on its railway locomotives and railcars. This box van, operated by Mrs M. Smith & Sons was fitted with a Gardner 4L2 engine.

BELOW: A forward control Tilling Stevens six-wheeler in service with Chivers that was powered by a Gardner 5L2 engine. Tilling Stevens was one of very few chassis makers that would willingly cast the names of its customers into the radiator header tank.

RIGHT: James Bowen & Co. of Musselburgh were Gardner agents for east Scotland and replaced the petrol engine in this Straker Squire lorry with a Gardner 4L2. A robust looking lorry, but like many other marques of that era Straker Squire vehicles were heavy. This one had an unladen weight of 5.25 tons giving less than 7 tons legal payload. Within 5 years of this photo being taken newly introduced eight-wheelers would weigh 7 tons empty for a legal payload of 15 tons, sounding the death knell for smaller, expensive, makers such as Straker Squire, Pagefield, Tilling Stevens, and Armstrong Saurer.
(Photo: C. & F. McKean)

BOTTOM RIGHT: In the early 1930s Karrier Motors of Huddersfield was quite a large commercial vehicles manufacturer. It was active in goods and passenger vehicles markets, and in particular the latter sphere. A Gardner 6L2 engine was fitted in this single deck Karrier bus, operated by Huddersfield Corporation and LMS Railways Joint Services. This was a large power unit for a single decker; no doubt it was specified to give extra power in the hilly and challenging terrain of west Yorkshire.

is a climb of 1 in 7 and a fully loaded Pagefield lorry was recorded as completing the ascent in second gear without its Gardner 4L2 suffering any undue stress or overheating. This same engine was sent back to Barton Hall two and a half years later, after completing 115,000 miles, for inspection. There was some cylinder bore wear of 0.014 to 0.017 inches; the exhaust valves needed renewing, and one or two fuel injection pump components were slightly worn. Other than these items the engine was in excellent condition with the pistons, bearings, and crankshaft journals all being as good as new. After the engine was re-assembled with a newer type of water pump and a replacement set of sprayers, it was returned to service.

Gardner's never envisaged automotive duties for L2 engines, but they immediately realised there was unlimited potential in this new market. Development commenced on a purpose built range specifically for commercial vehicles. These engines would have removable sumps for access from below, and would be lighter and more compact than L2 types. The pioneering L2s continued in production for their original purposes of marine and industrial propulsion and were hugely popular and successful at home and overseas.

RIGHT: The single cylinder Gardner 1L2 was used for a variety of applications. It also became a standard reference engine because of its efficiency and was used by oil companies and technical colleges for testing purposes. Note the intricate monogram of the company cast into the side plate.

BELOW: An early 6L2 unit rated at 60 bhp at 1,000 rpm. The marine ancestry of this design is evident with the large removable crankcase side plates, (a necessary requirement for Board of Trade regulations), to enable the main bearings to be inspected annually.

The Gardner L2 range unexpectedly opened a door for the company for automotive applications, and also in 1930 the first rail traction installations were made. Typical of these was this Drewry Standard Type 6/7 Ton diesel, shunting locomotive fitted with a 4L2 engine. It had a hydraulic coupling for a Wilson-Drewry 4-speed epicyclic transmission.

By autumn 1931 Gardner's were ready to commence production of their first purpose built automotive diesel engines. This was the fabled LW range and it retained the same cylinder bore and stroke dimensions of the L2 design. Apart from the combustion chamber pattern, very little else was common between LW and L2 engines. Gardner LW power units were higher revving with larger mains and big end bearings. Extensive use of aluminium alloy reduced their weights considerably, plus they were also more compact. Cast iron cylinders and cylinder heads were retained but the pistons were made from a special aluminium alloy. Cylinder liners, which were dry types, were renewable. Light aluminium alloy was also used for the one-piece crankcase. Once again the LW series was designed for two, three, four, five, or six-cylinder configurations. (An eight-cylinder version became available several years later in 1946). Individual

cylinder heads were not used on LWs, but were cast for covering either two or three cylinders. On a "like-for-like" basis LW engines were some 20% lighter than L2 units of an identical number of cylinders. Typically, for road going purposes LWs were governed at 1,700 rpm with an output of 17 bhp per cylinder at maximum revolutions. The power to weight ratio of an LW engine was approximately 15 lbs per bhp and fuel consumption proved to be even less than L2 types, with a figure of 0.370 lbs per bhp per hour being quoted.

The prototype LW engine, a six-cylinder, was completed in June 1931. It was used for experimental purposes for several years before becoming a static exhibit at the London showrooms of Norris, Henty, & Gardners. The first production LW engine is recorded as being tested on 6th October 1931. It was a 4LW (serial number 29259) and was destined for Peerless Lorries. The

next four 4LWs despatched from Barton Hall were all sold to individual operators for replacing petrol engines in existing chassis. Included among the purchasers were well-remembered heavy hauliers E.W. Rudd. An appointed Gardner's dealer, Toft and Tomlinson, carried out some of these conversions. On 1st December 1931 Tilling Stevens Motors received the sixth 4LW, number 29309. Walsall Corporation Transport bought the eighth 4LW, serial number 29313, on 5th January 1932. It was rated for 68 bhp at 1,700 rpm.

Production Gardner 6LW engines were set for 102 bhp at 1,700 rpm. Engine number 29240 was the first to be completed and on 26th October 1931 it was sent to Karrier of Huddersfield for fitting into one of their chassis. On the same day another 6LW left Barton Hall for Scammell of Watford, (number 29250). Less than a week earlier Guy Motors of Wolverhampton, had

Another early customer for L2 engines in 1930 was The Avonside Engine Co. Limited of Bristol. They installed a Gardner 6L2 unit in this twin bogie, 4-axle shunting locomotive. (Photo: The Avonside Engine Company)

Another Manchester company, Crossley, supplied passenger vehicles to several municipal city fleets in northern England including Leeds, Sheffield, and its local Manchester undertaking. All these concerns had fitted Gardner 6L2s into Crossley buses by the end of 1930 and this was a typical installation. 6L2s were relatively long units so the large capacity radiators protruded a considerable distance. When Crossley's started making its own oil engines they were beset by reliability problems.

received engine number 29252. This particular 6LW was fitted into a lorry bought by a Mr Barlow of Cheadle Hulme. On the same day as the order for Guy Motors was despatched, 20th October 1931, engine number 29261 and the fifth 6LW to be completed was sent over the Pennines to Leeds Corporation Transport. This undertaking installed it into a double decker, claiming to be the first municipal authority to test a LW powered bus. Tilling Stevens Motors ordered the fourth 6LW, number 29256, and it left Patricroft on 27th October 1931. Finally, to round off a busy last few days in October 1931, Foden of Sandbach took delivery of the sixth 6LW, number 29267, on the 30th of the month.

Five-cylinder Gardner LW engines started to appear in November 1931. The earliest recorded, (serial number 29269) was rated for 85 bhp at 1,700 rpm. On the 5th November it was sent to the London General Omnibus Company (L.G.O.C.), the capital city's largest operator, for fitting into a Leyland 'CC' bus chassis. After a lengthy period of

testing it was returned to Gardner's and it saw further service in one of the company's own lorries. At that date L.G.O.C. still owned AEC, suppliers of many of its buses, so Gardner's were not encouraged. Walker Brothers of Wigan took delivery of the second and third 5LWs, engine numbers 29274 and 29285, on the 24th and 20th of November respectively. They were installed in Pagefield lorries.

In November 1931 Gardner's exhibited for the first time at the Commercial Motor Transport Exhibition held at Olympia. New engines were on show with 6LWs being prominent in a Guy Goliath six-wheeler and a Karrier Consort double decker bus. Some chassis builders had Gardner power units in exhibition vehicles on their own stands. Foden of Sandbach, still a committed builder of steam wagons at that time, did have a six-tonner on show with a Gardner 6L2 power unit. A similar capacity Pagefield had a 4L2 fitted, and a 5L2 unit powered a six-wheeler Plantagenant from the same manufacturer.

Initially Gardner's concentrated

Gardner 6L2 engines also attracted the attention of railcar builders and one such engine was used in this motive unit and trailing car set for the Clogher Valley Railway. The design would never win any awards for attractive styling, but no doubt it was functional. It was built by Walker Bros.

on four, five, and six-cylinder LW engines for automotive applications. One sales brochure written in February 1932 provides interesting reading when it makes the claim that LW engines were preferable for passenger vehicles, but L2 power units were, in Gardner's opinion, better for heavy lorries. To back up their statement there were at that date just over 250 Gardner L2 powered vehicles on the road. Almost 200 were lorries; the remainder buses. In reality LW engines became much sought after by lorry operators by virtue of lower weight and higher power. The weight issue became even more important in 1933 when a new Road

1361

Transport Act and Licensing Regulations were enacted. As a result of this legislation it became vitally important for chassis manufacturers to reduce the weight of vehicles, and lorry operators desired a light chassis to maximise payload within gross weight limits. Lightweight Gardner LW engines were eminently suitable for this purpose. Incidentally, of the larger diesel engine manufacturers introducing new designs in the early 1930s, Leyland Motors also used a high percentage of aluminium alloys in its power units announced in 1933. Unlike Gardner LWs, Leyland diesels of that era had overhead camshafts and were made in either four or six-cylinder versions. Initially these were indirect fuel injection power units, but by 1934 they had switched to direct fuel injection. Even so, this was almost five years after Gardner's and their revolutionary L2. At Southall, AEC took even longer to embrace direct injection. It was not until 1937 that AEC engines had this feature as standard.

ABOVE: Industrial, or static applications were also commonplace for Gardner L2 engines. A 4L2 was used to power this clay excavator in service with a brickworks. The machine was built by Stothert & Pitt of Bath.

TOP RIGHT: Walker Bros. of Pagefield Iron Works, Wigan was an important customer of Gardner's in the early 1930s. Not only did they fit their engines into their Pagefield lorries, they were also builders of railcars powered by larger Gardner units. Unfortunately Pagefield lorries did not survive after the 1930s, (although specialised designs such as refuse vehicles were made after the Second World War). Railcars continued to flourish and this rather streamlined design for its time was supplied to Emu Bay Railway. It was driven by a 6L2 engine. (Photo: P.W. & L. Thompson Ltd. Coventry)

BOTTOM RIGHT: A rather more functional design of railcar typical of 1930s styling. Unfortunately no details were recorded and its size of Gardner engine is unknown.

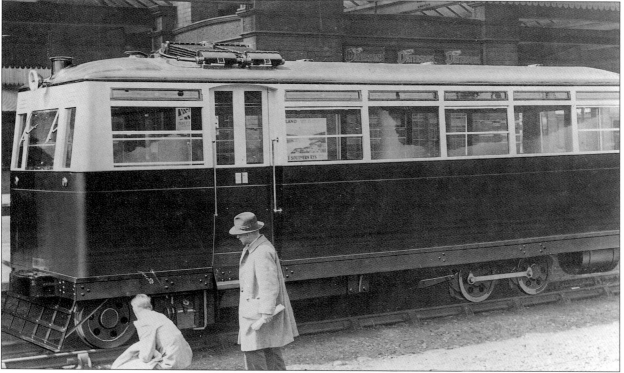

RIGHT: Within 2 years of the L2 range making its debut in 1929, Gardner's had introduced its fabled LW series of lightweight engines specifically for automotive applications. The destiny of the company was now determined and LW engines were to set standards for efficiency and reliability unmatched by most rivals for the following quarter of a century. A 4LW originally produced 68 bhp at 1,700 rpm.

BELOW: The high aluminium alloy content of automotive LW engines is apparent in this stand-mounted 6LW for producing 102 bhp at 1,700 rpm. The use of light alloys contributed to the low weight of these engines. Note the distinctive Gardner / CAV fuel pump with individual priming levers, and shaft driven dynamo.

4 LW ENGINE
68 BHP at 1,700 r.p.m. 5·6 litres capacity.

6LW ENGINE
102 B.H.P. at 1,700 r.p.m. 8·4 litres capacity

Albion Motors of Scotstoun, Glasgow, produced very high quality commercial vehicles but did not make a satisfactory diesel engine in the early 1930s. A Gardner 6LW powered this Albion double decker supplied to the independent company, Baillie Bros. Ltd. of Dumbarton.

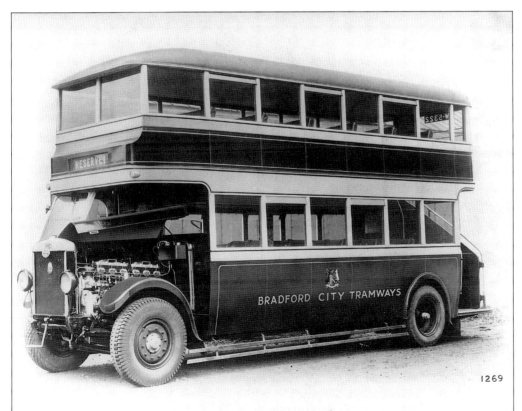

If the Gardner L2 engines proved the viability of diesel engine propulsion in road vehicles, then LW units positively confirmed that it was the way forward for larger commercial vehicles, and bus fleets in particular. Bradford City Tramways removed the original petrol engine from this Leyland Titan and installed a Gardner 6LW in its place.

103

Such were the demands for automotive engines that it was late May 1933 before the first Gardner 3LW unit was tested. This was engine number 30449 and on the thirtieth of the month it was fitted into Gardner's own Vulcan 30 cwt lorry. It produced 51 bhp at 1,700 rpm. The 2LW version was never used for normal road-going applications and the first did not appear until 1946. It was fitted into small road rollers and had other specialised industrial and marine roles. In common with standard Gardner practice LW engines were utilised for various purposes in addition to powering vehicles. Industrial and marine versions were available and for marine installations cast iron construction was an option. (The marine 2LW was only available in cast iron). Purchasers could specify their preference of either aluminium alloy or cast iron crankcase. Aluminium marine propulsion LW engines also had Gardner reversing gear casings cast from the same alloy. This company policy of offering a comprehensive range of options for every type produced explains why each Gardner engine was always an "individual" and the firm could never introduce mass production techniques.

By early 1932 several more chassis builders were offering Gardner engines as either standard fittings or options. In addition to Guy, Karrier, Foden, and Pagefield, who had vehicles with Gardner power units at Olympia in November 1931, the following manufacturers offered them: Scammell of Watford, Tilling Stevens Motors, Bristol,

A decision to manufacture 5-cylinder automotive diesel engines might be regarded as somewhat idiosyncratic, when perceived wisdom of the time was either 4 or 6-cylinder units. Nevertheless Gardner's introduced their 5LW in November 1931 and at 85 bhp at 1,700 rpm it soon gained acceptance with operators of both buses and lorries. David Brown of Huddersfield supplied many of the gearboxes mated to Gardner engines, and 5LW engines were to remain in production for almost the next 40 years. Gardner's were unique among British automotive engine manufacturers in offering this cylinder configuration.

A front entrance Daimler single decker with Gardner 5LW engine supplied to the City and Royal Burgh of Edinburgh. Daimler of Coventry was an important customer of Gardner's for many years.

Scammell of Watford was a British lorry builder that had its own distinctive ideas of how things should be done. It pioneered articulation in this country, although its articulated 6-wheelers (and later 8-wheelers) were conceived as complete units. For the first decade of production, Scammell used its own 7 litres, 4-cylinder petrol engine. The much better economy offered by Gardner diesel engines soon superseded the Scammell engine and this chain driven, solid tyred tractor was fitted with a Gardner 6LW. Tyre tread was obviously irrelevant in the early 1930s if the offside front wheel is examined!

Daimler, Maudslay, Shefflex, Vulcan, Dennis, Peerless Lorries, and Birmingham Carriage and Wagon Company. Even market leaders of the industry such as AEC and Albion were willing to fit Gardner engines if customers wanted them. Such was the reputation gained by Gardner's in a very short time that it soon became apparent that for the smaller commercial vehicle chassis manufacturers to succeed they would have to fit Gardner engines.

When a re-organised Atkinson Lorries (1933), and newly founded ERF both started to build lorries in 1933 they turned to Gardner's for engines. Atkinson of Walton-le-Dale, Preston, had evolved from making steam wagons, and then for a period it offered third axle conversions for two axle chassis from other makers. It produced its first diesel-engined lorry in 1932 and this had a Dorman 4RBL power unit. Soon Gardner LW engines were specified, leading to success for the company.

A boardroom disagreement over the merits of diesel propulsion against steam power led to Edwin R. Foden leaving his family's firm to found ERF Limited in 1933. A Gardner 4LW engine powered the first ERF lorry chassis. Gardner's, who supplied engines on six monthly credit terms, a facility never allowed to any other customers, supported Edwin Foden. Gardner's also took a small shareholding in ERF, a state of affairs that was to exist for the next forty-odd years, but never

ABOVE: With LW engines being preferred for automotive applications by the mid-thirties, the heavier L2 range remained popular for rail traction and marine installations. This 6L2 powered Bagnalls shunting engine was destined for overseas, and the Ashanti Goldfields Corporation Ltd.

TOP LEFT: Gardner LWs soon became the preferred option for Scammell buyers and a 6LW powered this articulated 8-wheeler for Redburns of Enfield. Again it was chain driven but shod on "balloon" tyres.

BOTTOM LEFT: Sidney Guy of Wolverhampton was another chassis manufacturer that relied heavily on Gardner engines for lorries and buses. A purpose built furniture removals van; this vehicle could have been built on a bus chassis to provide a low floor height. It also had a crew compartment behind the normal cab.

This is an archives find that adds an interesting facet to an illustration. The M.V. "Mirimar" was an Australian passenger boat, 90 feet long, with a Gardner 6J8 engine giving 228 bhp and 12 knots speed. On the rear of the picture, dated 23rd November 1934 is the following: - "M.V. 'Mirimar' on the Brisbane river. Wishing you and Mrs Houghton a merry Christmas and a very happy New Year. Kindest regards from Mr. & Mrs E.R. Hayles". Just who the signatories on the print were is not recorded, but of course Gordon Houghton was a Director of Norris, Henty, & Gardners Ltd. at that time.

made public knowledge before. Foden did not take too kindly to Gardner's supplying their upstart rival, so they sourced alternative diesel engine supplies. In the early thirties there were very few proprietary diesel engine options, but Foden tested Dorman power units. While these proved to be excellent marine and industrial engines they were unsuitable for automotive applications and customer demand forced Foden to revert to Gardner's. Incidentally, several years later during the Second World War, Foden received assistance from the Admiralty to develop a marine two-stroke diesel engine. The Navy took these in some quantity and Foden modified the design for road going purposes after the war. This engine was fitted in Foden goods vehicle chassis for many years, but Gardner units continued to be offered as options for operators concerned about better fuel economy and reliability.

As vehicle builders rushed to embrace diesel propulsion many attempted to adapt their own petrol designs for the purpose. Examples of this approach included Albion, Bristol, Daimler, Dennis, Tilling Stevens, Maudslay, and Crossley. None of these were successful at first, and some never were. Guy at Wolverhampton experimented with Meadows engines, whose factory was very near to their own. All these chassis makers were soon forced to buy from Barton Hall Works, but mass production was an anathema to the Gardner family so waiting lists for engines became normal. One famous company, Thornycroft of Basingstoke, ordered a few LWs and offered to fit Gardner units exclusively if the name 'Thornycroft' was cast onto the engines. Gardner's were definitely not impressed by that suggestion and nothing came of the proposal!

Word had soon spread among transport companies about the attractive fuel cost savings that could be gained from diesel power. The conversion market from petrol to diesel engines became very buoyant and in particular, the Gardner 4LW was a popular replacement choice. It was calculated that the £300-£350 costs

TOP RIGHT: If the Gardner 5LW was an unusual, but ultimately highly successful automotive unit, then the 3LW version was even more quirky for road going vehicles. It was used for a few Vulcan 30 cwt models, including one in Gardner's own fleet. However, 3LWs were popular in industrial roles, including a type of small excavator made by Smiths. Illustrated is an automotive version complete with David Brown gearbox.

BOTTOM RIGHT: The motor yacht "Aloha", built in 1932 by Vosper & Co. Ltd., Portsmouth. It was fitted with twin Gardner 4L2 engines. (Photo: Vosper Thornycroft [UK] Limited.)

of such a change would soon be repaid by a combination of cheaper fuel and significantly reduced consumption. Even if a conversion was financed by hire purchase the monthly repayment could be met simply by the costs of fuel saved on weekly distances of 500 miles or more. The vehicle operator only needed to find an initial cash deposit.

To educate fitters only familiar with petrol engines Gardner's organised courses of one-week duration at Barton Hall. Within five years of the introduction of LW engines the company's records state that no fewer than forty-six makes of commercial vehicles covering almost two hundred model variants had been converted to Gardner 4LW propulsion. These were a combination of British, European, and American marques.

By the mid-1930s the reputation of Gardner engines had spread to continental Europe. Back in the days of large Gardner two-stroke engines the Patricroft firm had experienced difficulty in lubricating little end bearings successfully. This was because there is no reversal of load on the little end with a two-stroke design. Kromhout, a well-known engine maker from Holland, solved this problem by letting the gudgeon pin slide sideways in the connecting rod eye. They allowed Gardner's to adapt this idea. Consequently Kromhout applied to build Gardner LWs under licence and agreement was reached with a royalty of just over £4 per engine. Similar licensing arrangements were made with Miesse in Belgium, FN, also of Belgium, and the French companies Bernard, and Latil. The licensing fee varied with the size of the company and the projected output of engines. For example, Miesse paid £3,600,

Thomas Gardner, 1860–1937.
A brilliant engineer who brought his family's firm into a new era by designing its earliest internal combustion engines in 1894, and lived long enough to see the company established as the leading maker of high-speed direct injection diesel engines.

and Bernard £12,778. The latter made 1,232 engines. Bernard also believed they knew more about fuel injection equipment than Gardner's and designed their own sprayers. Interestingly none of the continental Gardner engines achieved quite the exceptional fuel economy of Barton Hall units. This was thought to be as a result of different manufacturing processes. All the licensing agreements were terminated after the Second World War ended.

The Gardner LW engine range was to set standards for British diesel engines for the next generation when judged in terms of fuel economy, reliability, and longevity. Over the course of time there would be more powerful commercial vehicles engines than Gardner's, but the 'long stroke' characteristic always meant that a Gardner would pull well at low revs and happily

"slog away" on any hill climb. It would probably take slightly longer for a heavily laden lorry to reach the summit, but any driver was confident of getting there. In 1931, in the infancy of diesel engine propulsion, it was a truly remarkable achievement of Gardner's to produce an engine that would be able to compete virtually unchanged for the next thirty years. Its basic design was correct and efficient from the very first, whereas other engine manufacturers produced many types during the 1930s. Each one usually offered some improvements over its predecessor. But the Gardner LW range was good enough from the beginning. The achievements of the Gardner family with firstly their L2 engines, and then their LW range, and the revolutionary impact they had on road transport in this country has never been fully acknowledged. They changed the economics of moving goods and people; in itself a magnificent accomplishment.

Perhaps some individuals did recognise the contribution made by Gardner's. No less an authority than Sir Harry Ricardo, designer of the World War One tank engine, commented at a dinner of the British Association of Engineers in 1936: –

"…Early imported continental diesel engines had disappointed, for their noise, smoke and smell were intolerable, whilst their heavy maintenance costs went far to counter their advantage in the way of fuel costs…. Gardner's achieved in (1928 or) 1929 what no other firm in the world had succeeded in making, viz., a small high-speed open-chamber engine with a multiple-orifice injector which was consistently reliable. The Gardner engine stood in a class by itself thanks to the meticulous skill and care in its design and to superlative workmanship".

MEETING UNPRECEDENTED DEMANDS

Such rapid success in a new market resulted in further massive expansion at Barton Hall and soon the numbers employed exceeded 1,000 once again. By the end of the 1930s, with orders for LW and other Gardner engines having increased steeply every year, the labour force totalled 2,800 employees and the workshops covered 36,351 square yards. In the year 1931 just twenty-nine LW engines were made, but this number increased one hundredfold as commercial vehicle operators replaced petrol engines with diesels, and manufacturers who needed proprietary power units recognised the merits of Gardner's products. Once again many additional workers had to be recruited and trained, but the company coped very well and the highest quality was consistently maintained.

As the LW range and other new types created unprecedented demands on Gardner's some of the "old faithful" designs were finally phased out. The last 'F' type (serial number 4AF/25398) was tested on 8th August 1931, with the final 'M' type, (number 2FHM/30631) being assembled on 19th August 1933. Gardner 'M' types had remained in production for over thirty years and had been instrumental in establishing the company's reputation for premium quality. By the middle of the decade when automotive engine

GARDNER ENGINE 153 B.H.P. at 1200 R.P.M. with WALKER Flywheel and Clutch Housing and 125 m/k COTAL 4 Speed Gear Box.

Gardner 6L3 engines were popular choices for marine main propulsion in fishing vessels, and also as rail power units. With an output of 153 bhp at 1,200 rpm from 18.135 litres for railcars they operated well within their capabilities and were relatively unstressed to give long operational lives. This rail traction 6L3 illustrated here, from 1940, had a Walker flywheel and clutch housing with a Cotal 4-speed gearbox.

ABOVE: Largest engine in the L3 range was the 8-cylinder version of 24.175 litres capacity. For marine main propulsion duties they produced a very conservative 126 bhp at 800 rpm and gave trouble-free operation for years. The engine shown has a Gardner No.3 U.C. 2:1 reduction gear for marine duties.

RIGHT: A close-up shot of the interior of a Gardner No.3 U.C. Reverse Gear. (U.C. means "Unit Construction", in other words the gearbox was bolted directly onto the engine). Note, this engine was equipped with an electric starter motor.

A Gardner 3L3 marine engine with No.3 reverse gear. This was the smallest engine in the L3 series and could be set to produce between 48 and 74 bhp (800 / 1,200 rpm) depending upon application.

sales were reaching previously unheard of figures further rationalisation became necessary. On 11th November 1935 'V' type engine number 1AV/34577 was the last of its kind to be tested. Almost twelve months later, on 22nd October 1936, the final 'CR' type, (number 3BCR/36800), was fired-up in the testing department. Another famous range to cease production was the semi-diesel 'T' (and 'VT') engine, with number 3T4/42248 being the last one to be despatched on 27th May 1938.

With such a vast increase in orders for Gardner engines came the necessity for re-organizing the sales function of Norris, Henty, & Gardners. Earlier, in 1921, Thomas Gardner had become Chairman in place of Edward Norris, who remained on the Board of Directors until his death in 1939. Captain Henty died in 1922. Pre-empting the growth in demand, during the late twenties regional offices had been opened at Glasgow and Manchester. The head office in London dealt with all established and potential customers in an area south of an imaginary line between the Wash and Bristol. The Scottish office of Norris, Henty & Gardners handled all of Scotland, with the remaining territory serviced by Manchester. Showrooms and branch offices were also to be found in Liverpool, Birmingham, Hull, and Newcastle-upon-Tyne. When sales of auto-motive engines really started to boom in the mid-thirties the Directors of the marketing subsidiary were forced to re-appraise the levels of commission paid to their representatives and eventually such payment schemes were phased out.

A separate company named Gardner Engines Ireland Limited was founded with an office in Belfast to cover both Northern Ireland and Eire. Appointed Gardner agents were present throughout the world and in particular Australia was well served with representation in each populated state.

It will be recalled from Chapter 5 that in the year 1930 Gardner's supplied a 6L2 engine to Hudswell Clarke of Leeds for powering a shunting locomotive. In the following year, 1931, a similar engine was installed in a railcar for the County Donegal Railway Company in Ireland. This is claimed to have been the first diesel passenger locomotive to go into service in the British Isles. Incredible as it might be to believe, but yet another major engine project was progressing concurrently with the extensive ongoing development programme for the LW range. This was for a larger industrial and marine series and on 1st September 1932 the first Gardner L3 engine was tested. It was a four-cylinder unit, serial number 29791. The L3 cylinder was of 5½ inches bore and 7¾ inches stroke, and engines of three, four, five, six, and eight cylinder configurations could be supplied. Interestingly a seven-cylinder 7L3 is listed in the spare parts catalogue, but none were ever made and it is believed that one of the record clerks must have possessed a fertile imagination! An

Three and four-cylinder L3 marine engines were used in smaller vessels such as inshore fishing smacks and harbour launches. This 4L3 also had a Gardner No.3 reverse gear and depending upon the type of boat could produce between 63 and 100 bhp (800 / 1,200 rpm) from its 12.079 litres capacity.

8L3 engine produced 204 bhp at 1,200 rpm for rail traction purposes, but for marine and stationary uses a similar sized unit was de-rated to 126 bhp at 800 rpm. In 1939 this was increased to a standard 150 bhp at 900 rpm and there it remained for the next twenty-two years. Gardner L3 marine engines operated well within their design capabilities and because they were completely unstressed they had service lives of

prodigious longevity and reliability. Gardner's matched a specially designed reversing gear to L3 marine versions and this permitted the transmission of full power when going astern. This feature was greatly appreciated by fishermen.

One important customer for L3 locomotive engines was Walker Brothers, makers of Pagefield lorries. Walker's also made railcars and many were exported, taking Gardner products to railways in countries such as Australia, South Africa, and several in South America.

Within four years Gardner's had designed and developed three totally new engine ranges. But this was not a family firm content to rest on its laurels and another remarkable power unit was on the drawing board. Despite the growing popularity of LW engines for replacing petrol units and the preference for Gardner power from purchasers of many new

commercial vehicles, there was still a need for a smaller and lighter engine. Four-cylinder LW engines in particular were often chosen to replace petrol units in many kinds of lorries and buses, but even so, a 4LW was slightly too big for lorries with payloads of three to five tons. The 3LW variant was used in a small Vulcan model, but it never became a common option with operators. Lightweight types represented a high percentage of the total number of lorries on the roads in the thirties and to cater for this market yet another new Gardner engine was produced for the first time in the autumn of 1935.

This was the amazing Gardner 4LK engine and it represented an unusual diversion from established company practice. The 4LK was designed as a complete four-cylinder unit and not an engine series. It was made as light as possible with the

Illustration of a Gardner 8L3 rail traction engine which were normally set to produce 204 bhp at 1,200 rpm.

cylinder heads, and block, being cast from aluminium alloy. The pistons were also aluminium and the cylinder liners were cast iron. A special magnesium alloy was used for the crankcase and sump. All this resulted in an ultra lightweight engine which was also higher revving than anything previously made at Barton Hall. The traditional Gardner policy of a relatively long piston stroke was maintained with the 4LK. It had a stroke of 5¼ inches and bore of 3¾ inches giving a total swept volume of 3.8 litres. Early engines were set to produce 52 bhp at 2,000 rpm, but soon this was slightly increased to an output of 57 bhp at 2,100 rpm.

Interestingly the LK prototype made early in 1934, (serial number 31891), had been a six-cylinder engine. It was used for experimental purposes and 6LKs were never put into production. This important precursor of another acclaimed Gardner product was installed in an Invicta sports car. The first production 4LK, engine number 34405, was tested on 10th October 1935 before being exported to the Latil company in France. It was used to power one of their forestry tractors that was exhibited at a Paris show. Subsequent 4LKs went to Foden and ERF on 11th and 14th October 1935 respectively.

Gardner 4LK engines were an immediate success with smaller lorry owners and fuel economy was outstanding. Up to 25 miles per gallon could be obtained and because lightweight lorries were not restricted to the 20 miles per hour speed limit then in force, such vehicles were not only economical but productive as well. Even some owners of luxury cars installed 4LK engines in place of large and thirsty petrol units. A 1932 Lagonda was one that had such a conversion carried out and it is recorded that a fuel consumption of 42 miles per gallon was obtained with a highest top speed of 82 miles per hour. To supply this small, but no doubt profitable market, several "special edition" 4LKs were made for car installations. These were uprated to 85 bhp at 3,000 rpm and it is believed only forty of these engines were assembled. Such a high revving diesel engine was unusual in the 1930s and certainly broke with previous Gardner traditions and policy.

Latil of France, who was building Gardner engines under licence, took the 4LK design and used the LW

Gardner's achievement in producing four distinct engine types within a period of 6 years from 1929 to 1935 was truly remarkable. Every one was a proven winner and the 4LK was extremely innovative in its use of even lighter alloys than formulated for LW engines. 4LKs were intended for smaller commercial vehicles and the one shown in this picture was coupled to a Fuller 5-speed gearbox, not a very common option of transmission in Great Britain in the 1930s. Gardner's also had patented a 3-point flexible engine mounting arrangement for these engines.

bore dimension of 4¼ inches in place of the LK bore of 3¾ inches. The result was a powerful and compact four-cylinder engine, but unfortunately history has not recorded what Hugh Gardner thought about this idea!

With their LW range and 4LK available from the mid-thirties, Gardner's automotive engines were able to meet all the power requirements of vehicle builders. That is probably the reason why a 6LK version never went into production. When there possibly was a market for such engines many years later, there was simply insufficient capacity available at the works to consider making them. As it was, Gardner 4LK engines were also used for some industrial and marine purposes, especially during the Second World War.

The use of 4LK engines in cars followed a precedent set in 1932 when early 4LW engines were tested

in some cars owned by members of the Gardner family. Not only was this another means of evaluating engines, it also generated useful publicity for the company. By the late 1920s some of the founder's grandsons were active in the firm. Amongst them were Eric, the son of Mr Tom, and Hugh and John who were Joseph's sons. Being young men they took a keen interest in various kinds of motor sport. Hugh and John Gardner participated in motorcycle sand racing, a type of competition no longer held, but it was popular then and events took place on Southport beach. This period was also an era of numerous endurance tests and speed trials for cars, so it was logical for the young Gardner's to fit one of their engines into a suitable chassis for competitive purposes. They chose a 1925 Bentley as their test bed and it was an appropriate choice for a Gardner 4LW engine. From 1927 to 1930 W.O. Bentley achieved an

exceptional record of four consecutive outright victories in the Le Mans 24 hours endurance race. This prompted a barbed comment about the robust construction of Bentley's chassis from his great rival Ettore Bugatti. "Bentleys were the fastest lorries in the world" he remarked.

This Gardner powered Bentley was entered for several events but it first completed a test run to the Lake District on 5th February 1932. (Remember LW engines had only been in production for a little over three months). A motoring journalist accompanied Hugh and John Gardner on the journey and the fearsome Kirkstone Pass was one of the ascents tackled. In total they covered 171 miles and with the 4LW uprated to a maximum 2,500 rpm the car exceeded 80 mph. It returned a fuel consumption of almost 30 mpg and it was calculated that the cost for diesel fuel used was only one seventh of the cost of petrol for the same mileage.

While LW engines were intended for commercial vehicles it is interesting to speculate on the reasons why Gardner's decided to promote their new designs by installing a 4LW in a Bentley car. Was it purely for publicity reasons, or did they believe there was a future market to be tapped? Or, was it for development reasons to test the engine at higher revs? Whatever the reasons it made for a neat installation in this Bentley tourer. The comments of W.O. Bentley have not been recorded!

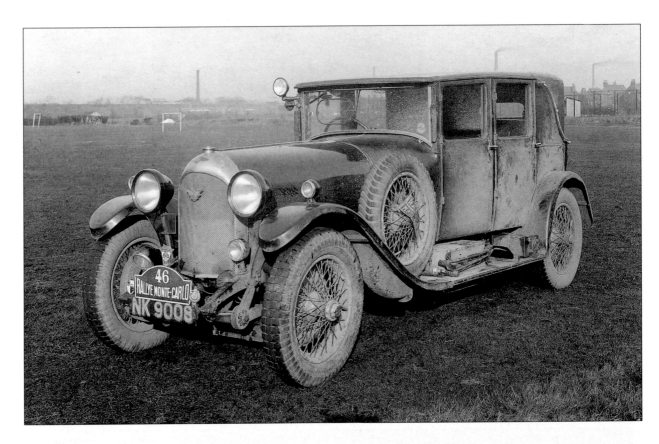

Gardner 4LK engines were fitted into several makes of larger cars, and special versions were produced specifically for such applications. They were uprated to produce 85 bhp at 3,000 rpm. Although this photograph was taken in 1961 it shows a 4LK in a Wolseley 21 saloon and is typical of a 1930s or 1940s car installation.

With the concept proven, the Bentley/ Gardner car was put through its paces at Brooklands where it lapped the famous banked circuit at 76 mph. Next it was taken to Shelsley Walsh for a hill climbing meeting and it reached the summit in 62.6 seconds. Both venues hosted prestigious competitions and these were the great days of British motor sport with all the well-known drivers of the time regularly taking part. To round off a busy year for the Bentley/Gardner during which it travelled 20,000 miles, it competed in and completed the RAC 1,000 miles rally with an average fuel consumption of 29 mpg.

But an even tougher test for a Bentley/Gardner combine was planned for early 1933. Another car was entered for the Monte Carlo Rally. This was probably the greatest international motor sporting event taking place in the thirties, and it retained its exalted status until quite recent times. The format of the rally was to have several starting venues throughout Europe with the conclusion in the principality of Monaco on the Mediterranean coast. Hugh Gardner could not spare time away from Barton Hall to take part; so chief driver was The Lord Howard de Clifford. The Bentley/Gardner was the first diesel-engined car to participate in the Monte Carlo Rally and it started from Tallyn in Estonia. Ahead was a journey of 2,350 miles across some of Europe's worst roads in severe winter weather. The car came through with flying colours being the first to the finish of seventy-two competitors that completed the rally. One hundred and eleven cars had started. The 4LW powered Bentley came first in its class on the Monte de Mules hill climb, it was the leading British entrant, and after all the results had been evaluated it was placed fifth overall. It was a terrific achievement and the press rightly

TOP LEFT: A notable triumph was recorded in 1933 when this Gardner 4LW powered Bentley came fifth overall in the prestigious Monte Carlo Rally. Driven by The Lord Howard de Clifford it completed 2,350 testing miles from Tallyn and was actually the first entrant to arrive at the finish. It was the leading British car and even Mr. Bentley must have been impressed by its performance. Photographed on its return to Barton Hall Works on the sports fields, still carrying its road grime, and with extra equipment on the running board.

BOTTOM LEFT: Although 4LK engines entered production in 1935, the prototype unit was in fact a 6LK that was tested in 1934. It was fitted into the chassis of an Invicta sports car, shown here, and could reach a top speed of 98 mph. Moreover, fuel economy was a highly respectable 35 mpg. Almost 70 years later these would still be creditable figures for a 6-cylinder diesel engine in a car. 6LK engines never entered production.

TOP RIGHT: The use of Gardner units in motorcars was little more than an interesting diversion from the main business of engines for commercial vehicles, marine, rail traction, and industrial uses. They were used in all kinds of machinery and a 5LW was fitted into this trenching excavator made by Allens of Oxford.

BOTTOM RIGHT: Any lorry built by Foden, ERF, and Atkinson would by the mid-thirties almost certainly have a Gardner engine. By then Foden had moved on from steam propulsion and had rejected other proprietary engines. Its own two-stroke design was some years in the future. John Smith's brewery of Tadcaster used this Foden DG lorry with drawbar trailer and while a 6LW would have been preferable, it is likely that a 5LW was fitted. (Photo: Author's collection)

acclaimed it as a triumph. Behind the bare statistics of the performance, impressive as they are, there was obviously a back-up team to lend support. For instance, diesel fuel could not be obtained from roadside service stations in those days; it was simply unavailable.

While Gardner automotive engines were designed exclusively for commercial vehicles, trials in cars such as the Bentley proved the reliability, viability, and economics of diesel propulsion. When the 4LK powered Lagonda was tested it returned a phenomenal 42 mpg on most journeys and on a special economy trial achieved almost 50 mpg at a steady 30 mph. Designers of modern diesel car engines of half the capacity of a 4LK obtain little more than this figure. This particular engine was later installed into a newer Lagonda and it went on to record 168,000 miles before being stripped down for inspection. The prototype 6LK could propel the Invicta at a top speed of 98 mph and typically returned 35 mpg. This engine was also fitted into a more modern Invicta chassis. Later, in the 1950s, a 4LK engine fitted in a Jaguar XK150 sports car achieved an incredible 90.85 mpg when competing in a Mobil Economy Run at Oulton Park circuit in Cheshire.

Gardner engines were exported to over forty countries and they were popular in many former British Empire and Commonwealth nations. In South Africa a 6LW was being installed into an unknown make of lorry when this photograph was taken. The man in the warehouse coat was recorded as a Mr. Ball, with the labourer a Mr. Anderson. (Photo: A. Roberts, Johannesburg)

TOP LEFT: This vessel is identified as "Lady Of The Isles" and was fitted with twin Gardner 6L3 engines. She was used in the waters around the Scilly Isles and her passengers were enjoying their trip on calm seas.
(Photo: James Gibson, Scilly Isles)

BOTTOM LEFT: The schooner "Cachabol" that was fitted with a Gardner 4L3 marine auxiliary engine producing 63 bhp at 800 rpm. In calm conditions when sails could not be used the engine could maintain a speed of about 6 knots.

TOP RIGHT: A Walker Bros. railcar powered by a Gardner 8L3 engine built for the Great Northern Railway.

BOTTOM RIGHT: Many Gardner rail traction engines were exported, either as part of shunting engines or railcars assembled in Great Britain, or supplied directly to overseas customers that built their own equipment. This Drewry Railcar four-car set was propelled by two 6L3 engines, each rated at 153 bhp at 1,200 rpm, and was in service in Tasmania.
(Photo: J.J.N. Barnett, Hobart)

The low cab on this Hunslet locomotive is typical of their design for underground working in mines. Gardner engines were popular for these locos because of their clean and spark-free exhausts. This was a pre-war type fitted with an 8L3 engine.

W 111

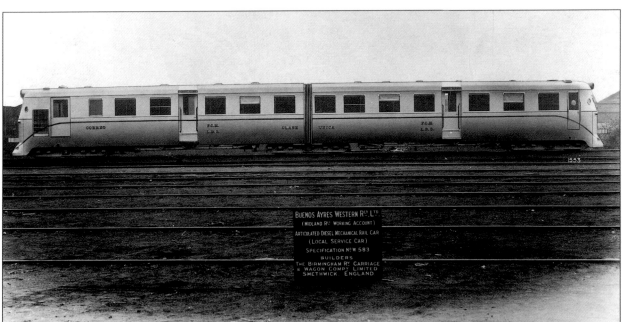

While L3 engines were the preferred type for rail traction, some Gardner LWs were occasionally used in this role. In November 1938 The Birmingham Railway Carriage and

Wagon Company Limited completed this articulated diesel mechanical railcar for the Buenos Ayres Western Railway Ltd. One 6LW engine was fitted at each end of the double railcar.

TOP LEFT: Kromhout of Amsterdam was one of five European engine manufacturers permitted to build Gardner direct injection diesel engines under licence before World War Two. Gardner's and Kromhout had collaborated in the late 1920s when the Patricroft firm had used the Dutch company's patented little end design for its 'J' type two-stroke diesel. Gardner's received a royalty of just over £4 per engine from Kromhout, which was not very much for an engine as large as the 6L3 used in this S.M. diesel locomotive. After the war none of the licensing arrangements were renewed.

LEFT: A late 1930s motor show in Paris with Gardner engines built under licence by Bernard exhibited on its stand. One 6LW is installed in a passenger chassis, and another is used as a display. One of the selling points listed, "Il ne fume pas" – it does not smoke!

In April 1939 a ceremony took place in Kampala, Uganda, to mark the introduction into service of 31 Gardner powered Albion buses by the Uganda Transport Co. Ltd.

337

By the mid-thirties Gardner's was undoubtedly enjoying tremendous growth and prosperity. The third generation of the family was now playing prominent roles in the firm's management and in 1934 Frank Gardner Wilkinson became Company Secretary and Director. He was the son of Elizabeth, (Lawrence Gardner's daughter), and therefore first cousin of Eric, Hugh, and John. In the year 1937 Thomas Gardner, – Mr Tom – died aged 76. He had remained active in the affairs of the company until a couple of weeks before his death. During his forty-seven years at the helm of Gardner's Mr Tom had driven the firm forward from their earliest internal combustion engines to their position as the world's leading diesel engine manufacturer. That was some accomplishment and he had provided the vision, enterprise, and technical know-how. When Thomas took over from his father Gardner's employed less than 100 men. At the time of his death the workforce

A Gardner 4LW industrial engine for driving an endless belt from the wide pulley. Of particular interest is the large lubricating oil reservoir and oil cooler mounted in front of the radiator.

numbered almost 3,000. There had been periods of expansion and contraction in his lifetime, but in 1937 Gardner's future was seemingly assured and the company was stronger than at any time before.

Edward Gardner became Chairman of L. Gardner & Sons Limited and Eric was appointed his Managing Director and Deputy Chairman. Joseph Gardner took over the chairmanship of Norris, Henty & Gardners. Apart from the legal necessities of titles being bestowed on senior Directors of a publicly quoted company, Gardner's retained their rather informal management style of never putting too many specific titles against other Directors and managers. The Gardner family dynasty was maintained after the death of Mr Tom with control of the company being firmly in the hands of the family and long serving senior employees.

As the 1930s drew to a close many commentators believed another European war was inevitable. At Barton Hall everything was still buoyant and demand for engines was insatiable. Gardner LWs were firm favourites with many lorry and bus operators. The 4LK satisfied the needs of lighter commercial vehicle builders and operators, in addition to being specified by

LEFT: The Second World War placed unprecedented demands on Barton Hall Works for engines for every conceivable purpose. This 4LW was used for a trailer searchlight set assembled by The Bristol Tramways and Carriage Company Limited. The engine generated 18/24 Kilowatts at 1,050 rpm.

Gardner stalwarts such as Foden, ERF, and Atkinson in smaller lorries. These Gardner designs were still some way ahead of engines from competing manufacturers when judged in terms of fuel economy, reliability, and longevity. Larger L3 series power units were gaining popularity with fishermen, and numerous of these were being ordered for railcars and shunting locomotives. Orders were still being obtained for the largest Gardner 'J' type engines to power craft such as ferries.

The outbreak of the Second World War in September 1939 caused even greater demands to be placed on Barton Hall Engine Works. This time there was none of the uncertainty that had been prevalent when war had been declared twenty-five years before in 1914. The works soon became a Protected Place under the auspices of the Ministry of Supply. The call was for Gardner engines of all types. The vast majority were destined for every branch of the armed forces that required motive power. Various marine units went into smaller ships such as convoy escorts and harbour defence craft. A specially constructed, seventy-two foot long harbour defence launch had twin 8L3 main engines plus a 1L2 auxiliary set. A few of these were also rigged with sails for the long voyage to the Caribbean, and became the last Royal Naval ships to carry sail. Plenty of Gardner marine auxiliary engines provided power for lighting and wireless transmitters in much larger warships such as destroyers. Even some aircraft carriers had emergency steering gear with Gardner units.

Gardner LW automotive engines were used in army lorries made by Foden and ERF. The famous

Scammell Pioneer ("Coffee-Pot") tank transporters were powered by 6LWs. Industrial units generated electricity for searchlights, wireless, and radar stations. Maunsell sea forts constructed strategically around the coastline and in river estuaries had Gardner 4LW driven generators and pumps. Shortages of raw materials during this period caused some changes to be made to Gardner's manufacturing processes. Aluminium was directed to aero engine manufacturers like Rolls Royce, and airframe assemblers, so many Gardner LW engines were made with cast-iron crankcases. As the war progressed virtually all Gardner's output went directly to the war effort, and any spare machining capacity was used for other tasks. For example, parts for anti-aircraft guns were made at Barton Hall.

During the Second World War women were once again recruited onto the shop floor at Patricroft. By then attitudes had changed and it became accepted practice to see females engaged in heavy engineering tasks. Some limited expansion was possible between 1939 and 1945 and just over 2,000 square yards of additional buildings were constructed. By the end of the war Barton Hall boasted 38,541 square yards of workshops. To provide a contingency in the event of fuel pump supplies from CAV becoming disrupted, Gardner's perfected their own design of injection pump.

Some further range rationalisation became necessary during the wartime years. On 22nd May 1940 the final 'J' type engine, serial number 4J5/49907, was tested. The last 'HF' type, engine number 12HF/54751, was completed on 10th February 1942.

Even relatively small 4LK engines had their purposes during the war, and no more vital mission was entrusted to them than propulsion and electricity generating for the midget submarines that crippled the menacing German battleship, "Tirpitz". Their ultra lightweight design, coupled with Gardner reliability, was essential in such small craft. Shown here are the engines that were part of a successful and heroic mission.

TOP: A trio of Gardner 6LW engines was used in RAF torpedo recovery launches which were triple-screw craft. Speed was of the essence in retrieving torpedoes before they sank. Unusually for marine installations, these engines were capable of their maximum power output of 100 bhp at 1,700 rpm. Gardner No.2 reverse gears were supplied and these were very powerful craft with a total of 300 bhp available.

ABOVE: A 1L2 marine auxiliary set for Admiralty 72 ft. harbour defence craft. These boats were usually powered by twin 8L3 Gardner engines, although some had Gleniffer main engines. The 1L2 produced 7 bhp at 700 rpm and these auxiliary sets comprised a special generator, ship's lighting generator, bilge pump, and air compressor.

Virtually every type of Gardner engine was used for some application during the Second World War. 4L2s such as this shown here were made for the Admiralty for fitting in 35ft. and 45ft. Survey Craft. They had a clutch and produced 40 bhp at 1,000 rpm.

A Gardner 6LW with U.C. reverse gear as used by the Admiralty for twin installation in 45ft. medium speed craft. These engines were set for an output of 85 bhp at 1,500 rpm and had special oil and water circulation and cooling arrangements to cope with continuous full power output.

Even little 2L2 engines had a role to play during the war and were used with Harland D.C. generators as standby radio power units on "Q" and "H" class destroyers. Complete with oil coolers and capacious radiators they were fully insulated and located against under water shock as per Admiralty requirements.

Much of Gardner's wartime output went to the Admiralty because of the Patricroft firm's extensive marine engine experience. This was another 6LW driven D.C. electricity generating set for 35 Kilowatts.

138

TOP LEFT: A 4LW skid-mounted radar set of a type used in many locations. Some were used as main or standby units at coastal radar stations; others formed part of mobile or static radar controlled searchlight batteries. Radar was a vital technological innovation during the war and was a contributory factor in the RAF's defeat of the Luftwaffe during the Battle of Britain in 1940.

LEFT: This 4LW unit construction generating set was for marine auxiliary and other purposes. It had a dual rating of 15/20 Kilowatts at 1,050/1,150 rpm. and was driving a G.E.C. dynamo. Again it was of a type with special oil and water-cooling arrangements and was fully insulated against under water shock.

One vital wartime task entrusted to Gardner 4LK engines was the propulsion of the midget submarines which crippled the German battleship "*Tirpitz*" in September 1943. This mighty warship was hiding in a Norwegian fiord posing a serious threat to Artic convoys bound for Russia. The midget submarines had to travel some 1,000 miles to press home their attack. The Gardner engines performed faultlessly and the mission was accomplished. Such was the bravery and gallantry of the crews that one Victoria Cross, two Distinguished Service Orders, and one Conspicuous Gallantry Medal were awarded. The importance of this mission was reflected in a letter the Admiralty felt compelled to write to Gardner's:

ABOVE: Twin Gardner 8L3 engines with U.C. reverse gears rated at 150 bhp at 900 rpm. These were installed in 72ft. harbour defence, anti-submarine patrol craft.

"The gallantry and skill of the officers and men who carried out this daring attack would have been to no avail if the weapon had failed. The fact that the material they used stood up so well to the strain placed upon it must reflect the greatest credit on the firms who made it and their work-people. The crews had every confidence in it, and it did not let them down."

TOP: Some special 6LW engines were made for mine sweeping duties and again had special water and oil circulation and cooling arrangements for continuous full output. Their Mawdsley dynamos produced 54 Kilowatts at 1,600 rpm and these engines were made to Hugh Gardner's approval and consent because of the severe operating cycles they were subjected to. When a pulse of electricity was switched it subjected the engine to a full load, leaving just enough time for it to build up power for the next charge. The consequence of this was the engine was always running flat out.

ABOVE: An Admiralty 72ft. harbour defence motor launch (HDML) complete with armament including depth charges. Power was from twin Gardner 8L3 main engines and an auxiliary 1L2 generating set. During the war three of these boats were sent to the Caribbean and to conserve limited fuel supplies on a long voyage they were rigged with mast and sails. It is claimed these were the last commissioned warships in the Royal Navy to carry sails.

TOP: One of the RAF torpedo recovery vessels fitted with triple Gardner 6LW engines. They were 60ft. long by 14ft. wide and this one was photographed on sea trials in 1938. During the war some of these craft were based at Hythe.

ABOVE: While the official Admiralty specification for its harbour defence launch was a length of 72ft., by some quirk of officialdom 6 were built 2ft. short at 70ft.! This is one of those shorter launches built in 1942 and with twin Gardner 8L3 main engines. After the war it was converted into the yacht seen here and named M.Y. "Skomer".

The following summarises the main purposes for which Gardner engines were used during the Second World War.

ROAD VEHICLES
- Army Transport Lorries Of All Descriptions. (Mainly Foden and ERF)
- Gun Tractors
- Tank Transporters, and tank recovery vehicles. (Scammell)
- Guy Passenger Vehicles

MARINE PROPULSION
- 'X-Type' Midget Submarine
- 72 foot Convoy Escort Craft
- 72 foot Harbour Defence Craft
- 45 foot Picket Boats
- 60 foot Torpedo Recovery Launches
- 26 foot Admiralty Survey Craft

AUXILIARY ENGINE SETS
- Radio Location. (Radar)
- Searchlights
- Gun Locations
- Aircraft Carrier Emergency Steering Gear
- Destroyer Emergency Lighting
- Admiralty Portable Wireless Stations
- Magnetic Mines Sweeping Sets
- Various Emergency Generating Sets For Ships
- Sea Fort Generating Sets

Throughout the period 1939 to the final Allied victory in August 1945 Barton Hall was producing at maximum output. In November 1943 Edward Gardner had died and Joseph succeeded him as Chairman in February 1944. When peace returned there would be no easing-up in demands for Gardner engines and waiting lists would grow longer in the years ahead as the company struggled to supply its customers with their requirements.

LW and LK ENGINE PRODUCTION 1931 to 1945

YEAR	3LW	4LW	5LW	6LW	LW TOTAL	4LK	TOTAL
1931		19	2	8	29		29
1932		268	52	155	475		475
1933	14	358	135	173	680		680
1934	45	633	564	297	1539		1539
1935	84	509	783	348	1724	38	1762
1936	20	429	1382	488	2319	279	2598
1937	4	555	1645	783	2987	269	3256
1938	1	510	1772	1056	3339	358	3697
1939	4	382	1595	885	2866	473	3339
1940	12	637	672	1137	2458	186	2644
1941	14	914	393	1052	2373	55	2428
1942	4	410	794	352	2560	20	2580
1943	0	354	1042	1546	2942	15	2957
1944	1	506	821	1772	3100	27	3127
1945	0	365	839	1634	2838	12	2850

NOTE:
Gardner's based production output on a total number of 'cylinders' made, so if a year by year comparison is taken with completed engine totals, it might not reflect the true picture. Output was influenced by the quantity of higher number cylinder engines. For example when more 6LWs were assembled the total of completed units could be lower than a previous year. In 1938 18,671 'cylinders' were produced compared with 16,872 'cylinders' in 1944. Only 9.63% less 'cylinders' but represented by 15.4% fewer completed engines. Remember also, multi-cylinder L2 and L3 engines were in great demand for marine and industrial uses in the war.

7

THE HEYDAY OF GARDNER ENGINES

ny fears that history would repeat itself after the return to peacetime following the Second World War proved groundless. It will be recalled that after the Great War ended in 1918 Gardner's enjoyed a brief period when engine sales remained good, before suffering a prolonged recession. This time around the demand for Gardner engines remained insatiable. And amazingly, this state of affairs was to become the norm for the next thirty years.

Barton Hall Works was released from the direct controls imposed during wartime by the Ministry of Supply. Even so, the Labour government elected in 1945 still influenced policy for companies such as Gardner's. After six years of war the nation was bankrupt. To restore its fortunes and obtain foreign currency, exporting of goods assumed great importance. The government decreed that half of every manufacturer's output should be sold abroad. Fortunately, Gardner's had been exporting successfully for over half a century and already had many overseas agents acting on its behalf. Eventually they would have representation in more than forty countries worldwide.

The prominence given to exporting meant that the home market was deprived of engines.

After the war there was a serious shortage of modern commercial vehicles. Production of lorries and buses for civilian purposes had been severely curtailed early in the war. Obviously some were made, for allocation to specified operators working under the control of the Ministry of War Transport. Many of these heavy lorries made by the smaller manufacturers Maudslay, ERF, and Atkinson were powered by AEC engines in place of Gardner's, which would have been the usual fittings had they been available. Such were the wartime demands made on the Patricroft firm that alternative power units became necessary. It is worth mentioning

Example of a post-1962 letterhead for Gardner Engines (Sales) Ltd., the company that replaced Norris, Henty & Gardners Limited. Directors were Hugh Gardner, John Gardner, William Bailey, Frank Wilkinson, and Dion Houghton.

GARDNER

Diesel Engines · Automotive · Rail Traction Marine & Industrial

BRANCHES AT
LONDON
ABFORD HOUSE, WILTON ROAD, S.W.I
TELEPHONES : TATe GALLERY 3315 & 3316
CABLES : GARDIESEL, LONDON, S.W.I
GLASGOW
124, ST. VINCENT STREET, C.2
TELEPHONES: CENTRAL 0887 & 0888
SERVICE DEPOTS
LONDON: 76,GT. SUFFOLK STREET, S.E.I
GLASGOW: 41, YORK STREET, C.2

TELEPHONES: ECCLES 2201-8
TELEX:
CABLES AND TELEGRAMS: GARDWORKS, ECCLES, MANCHESTER

GARDNER ENGINES (SALES) LTD

HEAD OFFICE & REGISTERED OFFICE
BARTON HALL ENGINE WORKS
PATRICROFT · ECCLES
MANCHESTER

YOUR REF _____

OUR REF _____ _____19___

Two Gardner L3 marine engines and a LW marine version on display at an exhibition in 1948. The venue was Earls Court, London.

that as early as 1937 AEC had designed a version of its famous 7.7 litre engine to compete with Gardner 5LW and 6LW units. Known as the AEC A202 engine, such a power unit had a bell housing compatible with a David Brown gearbox, the standard transmission with a Gardner engine.

Back in 1939 two of the leading passenger chassis builders were Leyland Motors and AEC. Within a few months of the declaration of war both these companies suspended bus and coach manufacturing to concentrate on military production. Once various coachbuilders had bodied their backlog of chassis no new buses were available. By mid-1942 it became apparent to the authorities that limited quantities of new passenger chassis for civilian transport were very necessary. Accordingly, a "Utility" specification for a no-frills bus was drawn-up and assembly was allocated to Guy, Bristol, and Daimler. These prominent marques had fitted Gardner engines at customers' requests during peacetime, but only Guy was permitted to use Gardner engines (with cast iron crankcases) in "Utility" buses. Both Bristol and Daimler obtained AEC 7.7 litre units until Gardner's became available once again towards the end of the war.

By the year 1946 many municipally and privately owned public transport undertakings were ordering large numbers of new vehicles. A similar situation was unfolding with road haulage contractors, although they were being more cautious because of uncertainties resulting from the impending nationalisation of road transport. Nevertheless, there was a tremendous home market demand for new commercial vehicles and the engines to power them. This was in addition to the export drive instigated by the government. But all manufacturing industries were beset by difficulties and problems. Many factories had been working to full capacity for the preceding six years and consequently machinery was worn and needed replacing. Servicemen and women fortunate enough to have survived the war returned to claim their jobs, but re-adjusting to civilian life took time. The biggest problems were caused by rationing and shortages of raw materials; situations which were to persist until the early 1950s. Gardner's were not immune from these challenges and clients ordering engines had to wait several months for delivery. One serious shortage nationally, which hardly affected Barton Hall Works, was that of electricity during the late forties.

This is a view of the inspection department at Barton Hall, taken in about 1950. Various small components such as small gear wheels, valves and valve rockers, etc. were examined here. Apparently women were provided with chairs with backrests; men had to be satisfied with wooden stools. However, note the high lighting levels. (Photo: Entwistle, Thorpe & Co. Ltd.)

Every industrial premises was subjected to power cuts, and consequently, loss of production, but Gardner's had its own power house with a variety of engines driving generators, enabling the works to be self sufficient.

By 1948 most of the important legislation for nationalising road transport, the railways, and the coalmines had been enacted. All this unprecedented industrial reform affected Gardner's in varying degrees. The hire and reward haulage industry came under the control of the Road Haulage Executive and its famous British Road Services (BRS) operating divisions. One of its declared aims was to standardise on certain classes of lorries for specific duties and types of traffic. Heavy-duty eight wheelers were the preferred long distance trunk vehicles and BRS ordered them from Foden, ERF, and Atkinson, all of which used Gardner engines.

When British Railways was formed it too was keen to rationalise the vast locomotive stable it inherited from constituent companies. There were numerous categories of steam railway engines and much smaller quantities of diesel-mechanical shunting types. Gardner engines powered similar locomotives made by Hudswell Clarke, Drewry, Walker Brothers, and Hunslet, usually for industrial railways in this country. Shortly after nationalization in 1948 British Railways acquired its first Gardner engined shunter. It was highly successful and within a few years virtually the entire class of British Railways' small diesel-mechanical shunting locomotives was Gardner powered.

It was a similar situation in the coal mining industry with modernisation and capital investment required. Thousands of pit ponies still toiled underground and most of them were eventually replaced with Hunslet mine locomotives. Gardner engines were used in many of these, but because of the heavy demands made on Barton Hall Works, sales to Hunslet and others had to be strictly rationed. Gardner engines were noted for clean and spark-free exhausts, causing them to be popular for underground environments. The latter attribute was also of great importance where pockets of potentially flammable and explosive gases could accumulate.

After the Second World War there were relentless demands for Gardner engines from its main outlets; automotive, marine, rail traction, and industrial. Walker Bros. of Wigan continued to be good customers and this is a close-up of a Walker patent central power bogie showing the propeller shaft, main gearbox, and vacuum servo for operating the gearshift. One of the two Gardner engines in the power bogie is in the background.
(Photo: P.W. & L. Thompson Ltd., Coventry)

As Gardner's began to settle down to peacetime and prosperity with the satisfaction of full order books for home and overseas customers they suffered the death of William Gardner in 1947. Mr Willie was the youngest son of the founder of the firm, Lawrence. Eric Gardner, then Deputy Chairman, passed away at the age of fifty only ten weeks after his uncle. But sad as such occasions were family continuity was maintained and Hugh Gardner was appointed Deputy Chairman to his father, Joseph. Other changes and appointments were made to the Board of Directors. Hugh and John Gardner became Joint Managing Directors and the long serving works manager, Harold Hunter, became Works Director with a seat on the Board. A new directorship was now granted to Dan Denholm, who was already a Director of Norris, Henty, & Gardner's. He became Commercial Director of L. Gardner & Sons Ltd. W. Bailey, Company Secretary of the subsidiary, was elected to the Board of the London based company.

Most of Gardner's competitors announced new engine ranges in the period between 1945 and 1951. Even though the Gardner LW design dated back to 1931 and their L3 range was of a similar age, the company had no plans to replace either. There was no need to, because in terms of reliability, fuel economy, and longevity Gardner engines still had the edge on any others. Improvements resulting from ongoing development work were used for new engines, and when older units were overhauled such modifications could usually be incorporated into them.

This policy encouraged operators to order more of the same with confidence, in the knowledge that their Gardner engines would not become obsolete overnight. In any case there was none of the built-in obsolescence so common nowadays. For example, an Atkinson or ERF eight-wheeler lorry built in 1946 with a Gardner 6LW engine, David Brown gearbox, and Kirkstall Forge axles would have been expected to be in service ten years later. And a new vehicle from both those assemblers would still have had an identical type of engine and driveline in 1956.

As the main Gardner types of LW, L3, and 4LK were able to cater for most applications some further rationalisation of their catalogue occurred. In 1949 the last petrol fuelled Gardner 'OVC' type was tested on 29th November. This was engine number 81269. Almost two years later on 25th June 1951 the last of the pioneering L2s was started-up in the testing department. This was engine number 4L2/87122.

ABOVE: The same Walker power bogie showing on the left a sprung cross bolster which supported one end of the rail coach. (Photo: P.W. & L. Thompson Ltd., Coventry)

LEFT: Another view of the Walker power bogie showing the sprung cross bolster, and both Gardner engines. (Photo: P.W. & L. Thompson Ltd., Coventry)

TOP: *A two-coach railcar completed for Tasmanian Railways in late 1948. A Gardner 6L3 engine at each end powered it.*

ABOVE: *An eight-cylinder LW variant did not appear until 1946, some 15 years after Gardner's devised its LW series. For automotive applications 8LW engines were* originally *set at 140 bhp at 1,700 rpm, but installations were few because the length of the engine exceeded the depth of lorry cabs of the time and protruded into the loading area. Atkinson built a few eight-wheelers with 8LW engines, and Foden assembled some heavy haulage tractors with these engines.*

ABOVE: Thos. Smith (Rodley), Yorkshire, was a good customer for Gardner engines, using various sizes in its range of cranes and excavators. This 6LW powered excavator was photographed in action in December 1950.
(Photo: Commercial Photo Services, Leeds)

LEFT: A smaller dragline excavator made by Smith (Rodley) driven by a Gardner 3LW engine. The lorry being loaded is a Bedford 'O' Type tipper, just one of thousands of similar Bedfords in service by 1950.

399

By the year 1951 many operators were demanding more power from LW engines. An eight-cylinder version had been introduced in 1946 but it was too long for most automotive purposes and protruded into the cargo carrying space of a lorry. By then Hugh Gardner was Chief Designer and he had very conservative views on engine power, believing economy and longevity were sacrificed if excessive horsepower was extracted from a cylinder. By then both Leyland Motors and AEC had introduced six-cylinder units, albeit of greater cubic capacity than a Gardner 6LW, capable of 150 bhp output. (For some export markets they were uprated to 165 bhp). These engines were in demand from BRS and some own account operators who pulled drawbar trailers behind an eight-wheeler lorry. Incidentally, the regulation prohibiting an eight-wheeler towing a trailer had been

rescinded as an emergency wartime measure in 1942. After the war the status quo remained and led to such lorry and trailer outfits becoming popular. Accordingly, AEC and Leyland eight-wheelers with their more powerful engines were better suited to drawbar trailer duties than similar lorries from Foden, ERF, and Atkinson with more modestly powered Gardner 6LW units.

In response to demands from operators Hugh Gardner agreed to uprate the power output of LW engines. At first there was a modest increase for a 6LW from 102 bhp to 112 bhp, (LW 'K' series), still at 1,700 rpm. Much later, in 1968, this was increased further to 120 bhp, equating to 20 bhp per cylinder. Such engines were designated LW20 and older units could be modified for higher power when they were overhauled. Increased power from all Gardner LWs was achieved by reducing internal friction, improving

exhaust flow, and by increasing injection pressures. Because of the customary meticulous attention to detail there was no increase in fuel consumption. Nor was there any loss of reliability or longevity. If anything both of these important parameters improved even more, as benefits were gained from continuing metallurgical advances, progress with manufacturing processes, and better lubricants became available from oil companies.

The arrival of more powerful LW engines in 1951 was accompanied by the announcement of a modern horizontal Gardner engine range. However, they were nothing like the old slow revving single cylinder industrial engines with their massive flywheels from a former age. These engines were based on vertical LWs and were designated HLW. They were intended for a new generation of underfloor-engined passenger chassis and railcars. Coaches with

LEFT: John Gardner commenced development work on horizontal LW (HLW) engines in 1950 and such units were ready for commercial applications in 1951. They were needed for the new generation of luxury coaches that had underfloor, horizontal engines, mounted in mid-chassis. They were also used in railcars in due course. Shown here is a 6HLW engine.

TOP & BOTTOM RIGHT: Two further views of a 6HLW engine and some indication can be gauged of the complex modifications necessary to a standard, vertical design. A completely different sump and oil filler was needed, and internal lubrication modifications were necessary. Also, some re-working of cooling jackets had to be carried out to overcome formation of steam pockets and potential cooling problems.

Gardner horizontal engines proved popular with traditional passenger chassis customers for new designs of luxury coaches. In 1956 the outright winner of the prestigious British Coach Rally at Brighton was this Bristol 32 seater coach with Gardner 5HLW engine. It was in service with Eastern Counties Omnibus Coy. Ltd. and the body was constructed by Eastern Coach Works.
(Photo: The Brighton Photographer)

engines under their floor, and mounted in mid-chassis, had been introduced in North America during the 1930s. These were recognized as the way forward for luxury, long distance passenger vehicles, but the war halted research in Great Britain

and Europe. Tilling Stevens Motors, (TSM), of Maidstone had exhibited such a chassis at the 1938 Commercial Vehicle Show with their own design of flat, horizontal eight-cylinder diesel engine. As a company TSM lurched from one financial crisis to another and their prototype lacked development. Little more was heard of this idea until it was revived by coach chassis manufacturers in the mid-1940s.

Apart from road going applications, horizontal multi-cylinder engines also offered plenty of potential as motive power units in railcars. So, John Gardner decided to develop a horizontal LW range of engines. It was not simply a case of turning vertical engines through eighty-eight degrees to achieve this, but a complex engineering problem. Lubrication of the moving parts had

to be re-worked and steam pockets in water jackets needed eliminating. The difficulties experienced by John Gardner were many and varied but all were eventually solved. The Gardner HLW series was a great success with over 4,000 engines being sold through the years.

John Gardner played many vital roles at Barton Hall. Being the younger brother, he had to submit in part to Hugh and at times differences of opinions resulted in serious arguments. Fortunately none of the rows got out of hand like they did at Foden's in the early thirties when Edwin R. Foden resigned and founded ERF in competition. (Incidentally, E.R. Foden received financial assistance from Gardner's for his new venture). Hugh Gardner dealt almost exclusively with Managing Directors of chassis

Gardner engines had first been used for portable compressors in the early 1900s and they were still sought after for these machines fifty years later. A 5LW was used in this quite large "Broomwade" compressor. Broom & Wade was one of the leading manufacturers of air compressors.

building customers while John was much more in touch with the broader spectrum of Gardner's other clients. He also produced the much needed instruction manuals for all the different engines, and later with his son Paul reorganised the very important spare parts department.

Hugh's main priority was the automotive side of the business and marine installations took second place, but John tidied-up the Gardner marine engines. Until he gave them his attention header tanks, heat exchangers, and seawater pumps were all separate items, requiring boat builders to mount them and provide pipe work. Once these components were supplied with the engine the complete package was far more attractive to purchasers.

As raw materials at last started to become more plentiful in the early fifties Gardner's were able to

maintain an annual production figure of 4,000 to 4,500 engines. There was no easing-up in demand and questions were even asked in the House of Commons about delays in satisfying orders. In particular some Scottish fishing fleets were awaiting Gardner engines and Robert Boothby M.P. (later Lord Boothby) asked if the Ministry of Supply could release to fishing boats engines earmarked for export. Norris, Henty, & Gardners were not slow in capitalising on this unsolicited testimonial from Westminster and had appropriate promotional literature printed.

Fishermen placed great faith in Gardner engines and this trust was instrumental in the first order from the Royal National Lifeboat Institution (RNLI) for lifeboat engines being received at Barton Hall in 1954. While annual sales of engines for lifeboats would remain

small, it was business carrying tremendous prestige. Most lifeboat crews comprised a high percentage of fishermen and they were familiar with Gardner engines, relying on them daily. They lobbied for their fitment in rescue craft, although Gardner's had supplied Trinity House with engines for generators in lighthouses and lightships for over thirty years. But until 1954 the Ferry Engine Company of Southampton made lifeboat engines, including a 6-cylinder diesel type. This firm's engines were special watertight designs, and only made in small numbers for the RNLI, causing them to be very expensive. The order received by Gardner's was for twin LW marine units, and they were installed in the Coverack Class *"William Taylor of Oldham"*. The self-righting lifeboat weighed 16.5 tons and it could cruise at 8.4 knots. Initially the RNLI had approached

A near neighbour of Gardner's was Ingersoll-Rand at Trafford Park, Manchester. Ingersoll-Rand also made portable compressors and used Gardner engines. Two sizes are shown here, the smaller driven by a Gardner 3LW, and the larger powered by a 5LW engine.

803

Gardner's envied reputation was enhanced even further when Hugh Gardner, with brother John's assistance, designed his 6LX engine in 1958. It was based on existing LW practises but incorporated many new features. Knowledgeable pundits in later years regarded the 6LX at 150 bhp as the finest Gardner automotive engine of all time. This fuel pump side view of an early 6LX shows many traditional Gardner features carried over from LW series units, and this engine had an 8 inches diameter dynamo.

Gardner's and asked for a completely watertight engine specification. Because no other commercial applications could be envisaged, Gardner's rejected the idea. Eventually the RNLI designed watertight engine rooms that could take standard Gardner marine units. The success of this installation resulted in most new RNLI deep-sea lifeboats having Gardner engines for the next 25 years.

An era came to an end for the family firm with the death of Joseph Gardner in 1955, aged 81. He was the last surviving son of the founder and a tangible link to the earliest days of 1868, the origins of the company. Joseph's eldest son Hugh replaced his father as Chairman, as well as still being a Joint Managing Director with younger brother John. Hugh and John also became Joint Managing Directors of Norris, Henty, & Gardners. Once there had been

eight Gardner family members on the main Board of Directors, but even with just two of them serving as Directors, control remained in their hands. However, Hugh and John Gardner made other appointments in the following twelve months to safeguard their family's position.

Hugh had been aware for some years that financial institutions had been buying shares in the company. With full order books and lengthy waiting lists for engines profitability was good and Gardner's was financially sound. Hugh Gardner was fearful that some of these larger shareholders would demand representation on the Board, which he did not want at all. Three years earlier in 1952 Dan Denholm, the Commercial Director, had suddenly died. He was badly missed, having had an excellent rapport with customers. Gardner's had very capable factory representatives in

most overseas markets, so to fill the gap left by Dan Denholm's death, Cyril Plane was recalled from Australia, where he had done an outstanding job, and he was promoted to Sales Director of Norris, Henty, & Gardners. It must have been quite a wrench for him to be stuck in an office at Patricroft under Hugh Gardner's thumb after being his own boss with all of Australia and New Zealand to roam around.

To counteract the threat of "outsiders" becoming Directors, three long serving Gardner's managers were elevated to the Board in 1956. They were Eric Bradshaw, who was Hugh's right hand man in the research department, W.G.T. Thompstone, and E.A. Todd B.Sc. Gordon Thompstone was Works Manager, and a qualified solicitor, with plenty of experience in negotiating with trade unions. Eric Todd was a technician.

RIGHT: Gardner's always insisted that its chassis-building customers installed engines properly. This three-quarters frontal view of a 6LX shows the patented self-contained flexible mounting arrangement using link type forward mounting that was combined with a rear supporting torque reaction member and hydraulic damper. This design permitted simple three point rigid attachment in a chassis.

BELOW: A partly sectionalised view of a Gardner 6LX '150' engine. Gardner's retained triplex timing chains when by 1958 most rival engine builders in the premium quality engine market had abandoned timing chains in favour of meshed gears.

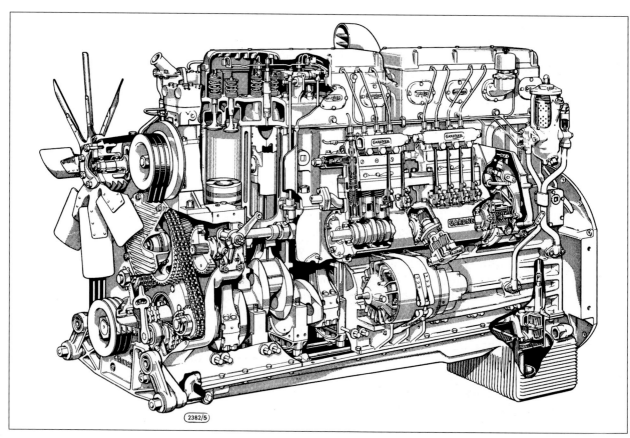

792

838

ABOVE: For the 6LX engine the traditional Gardner practise of using its own fuel pump cam box with CAV injection pumps was retained. Shown here are the injection pumps, cam box and governor unit that also carried the fuel lift pump, oil cooler pump, and tachometer drive unit. The priming levers were also retained.

LEFT: The intricacies of the Gardner 6LX governor arrangement can be seen with the covers removed on the rear of the fuel injection pump. Also visible are the accelerator and stopping levers, along with the engine sump oil level dipstick.

A novel feature used for 6LX engines was cross-bolts that went through the main and big end bearing caps from one side of the crankcase to the other. This increased the rigidity of the bottom end of the engine giving enhanced bearing life. The depth of the locating face of the bearing cap can be gauged with number 4 main bearing removed in this photograph.

There was one interesting development resulting from these main Board appointments of 1956. Brothers Cyril and Jack Plane had flown the flag for Gardner's since before the war in Australia and South Africa respectively. Each had been in overall charge of sales for the company in these countries, and as stated Cyril Plane was Sales Director of Norris, Henty, & Gardners. Cyril had learned his engineering trade with Garrett of Leiston, Suffolk, steam traction engine and agricultural implements makers. When Eric Bradshaw was appointed to the main Board of Gardner's Cyril Plane took umbrage and resigned from the subsidiary concern, believing that he should have been promoted because he was a vital link between the works and customers. He went to South Africa and joined his brother Jack, an equally outstanding factory representative, who was in charge of Gardner Engines S.A., which was also an engine reconditioning facility.

Cordial relations with Cyril and Jack Plane continued and some large

orders for mines locomotive engines were received at Patricroft. Jack had built a very prosperous business in Johannesburg, starting in 1936. He was quite inventive, even making cast iron crankshafts during the war to keep vehicles on the road after ships carrying spares had been torpedoed. He also foresaw the need for road trailers in South Africa and started an assembly line in his factory for units supplied in CKD format, and under licence, from Crane Trailers of Dereham.

It should be realised that Gardners' "friends" in the United Kingdom were principally Atkinson, Bristol, Daimler, ERF, Foden, and Guy. The "enemies" were Leyland and AEC, particularly in bus markets and efforts were always made to try and thwart the "enemies" in favour of "friends". AEC obtained a considerable amount of orders for buses in South Africa and to reduce import duty they exported them in completely knocked down chassis format (CKD). The most convenient place to assemble them was Jack Plane's factory, so he visited

Patricroft to seek consent from Gardner's Board to work with an "enemy". Fearful of their "friends" reaction to such a move Gardner's vetoed the idea, telling Jack that he could not serve two masters and he must choose one. Jack, with brother Cyril's backing chose AEC, but there was no acrimony, because Jack and Cyril Plane are remembered as a couple of the nicest people one could wish to meet.

It has to be said that Plane's agreement with AEC was extremely fruitful and that company enjoyed tremendous success in South Africa until the mid-1970s when the problems of British Leyland (of which AEC was a constituent company) caused the demise of the Southall firm. After Leyland acquired AEC in 1962, it later bought Jack and Cyril Planes' business, with Jack becoming one of the largest individual shareholders in British Leyland.

Back in 1956 it meant that Gardner's had to find new management for their South African subsidiary. Gardner Engines (South Africa) Ltd. became a branch of

CN. 119

Samuel Osborne of Sheffield, who had good connections there. Orders for bus engines continued to be won, along with sales of smaller power units. Patricroft stipulated that 2LW and 3LW engines had to be made in batches of thirty or more to make production worthwhile.

Cyril Plane was replaced as Sales Director by Dion Houghton. He was son of Gordon, who was a Director of Norris, Henty, & Gardners from 1926 until his death in 1954. Dion was a time served aeronautical engineer who learned his trade with the famous Supermarine company. He also spent two years on the shop floor at Barton Hall to discover what constituted a Gardner engine. Before re-locating to Patricroft, Dion was based at London office with exports responsibilities. Sales activities in all overseas regions were supported by factory trained technical representatives and engineers.

By the mid-fifties the road haulage industry had been partly de-nationalised and when a privately owned sector re-established itself lorry sales remained buoyant. Steady, repeat orders were also being received from passenger chassis manufacturers for Gardner engines, although this market had peaked after the post-war re-placement and renewal programme was completed. Public transport growth was at best static as car ownership became more wide-spread. Exports were still good, and marine and rail traction power units remained in demand. Gardner's were in a very strong position and waiting lists for engines were becoming longer. However, many chassis builders and operators were demanding higher power outputs to cope with heavier weights and a need for faster journey times.

If the eight-wheeler heavy lorry

In the 1950s Scammell was still producing lorries with its own distinctive styling and designs. They had changed little from those of 20 years before. This Scammell articulated 8-wheeler entered service with Tuff & Hoar Limited in 1949 and had a Gardner 6LW fitted.

market of the mid-fifties is analysed it can be seen why there was a potential problem in the offing. In terms of annual home market chassis registrations Leyland and AEC were market leaders, and of course both of them used their own engines. Albion and Thornycroft also built eight-wheelers with in-house made engines. The other main marques were Atkinson, ERF, Foden, Scammell, and Guy. All these fitted Gardner 6LW power units and their

At the formation of British Road Services one of its stated aims was to standardise its main categories of vehicles. However, because the organisation's monopoly lasted for only six years it could not achieve the standardisation it desired. It did influence several of the main lorry manufacturers in their designs and engaged the Bristol Carriage and Tramways Company, by then concentrating on passenger vehicles, to build eight-wheelers and tractive units to its own, BRS, designs. Eight-wheelers generally used Leyland engines with tractive units usually having Gardner power units. These photographs show the special air cleaner arrangements for Bristol tractive units fitted with Gardner 6LX engines and supplied exclusively to BRS.

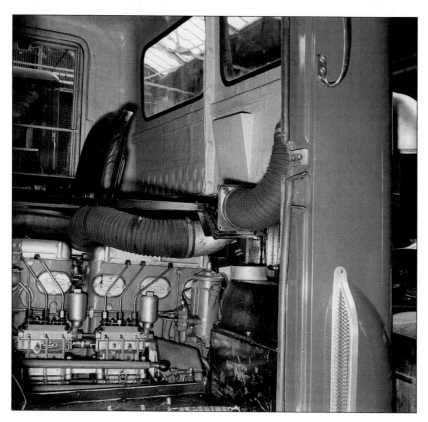

chassis production was limited to a greater or lesser extent by the lengthy waiting lists for engines from Barton Hall Works. To reduce delivery delays some Atkinson customers like Whitbread and Harold Wood specified AEC engines, but Gardner 6LWs powered the majority. Foden also offered its own two-stroke engine as an option. Seddon Diesel Vehicles Limited of Oldham was about to enter the heavyweight multi-axle lorry market and ordered its first Gardner engines in 1956. Therefore in total, more eight-wheelers were entering service every year with Gardner engines than with any other individual power unit. However, a Gardner 6LW at 112 bhp was considerably less powerful than an AEC 11.3 litre (150 bhp) or a Leyland O.680 (154 bhp). A very few Gardner 8LWs at 150 bhp were used in some eight-wheelers, but this was a very

CN.110

expensive (and not really practical) option. Leylands and AECs were quickly becoming the preferred choices for road hauliers that put drawbar trailers behind lorries. Also, in the year 1955 a revision of Construction and Use Regulations allowed a solo rigid eight to legally run at 24 tons gross weight. Some overloading was common so an 8.4 litres 6LW was becoming marginal, even for non-trailer duties. With a drawbar trailer as well up to 32 tons gross weight was permissible and at such weights the frugal and willing 6LWs were definitely too small.

During preceding years a relatively low power to weight ratio was not perceived as too much of a

problem. Road haulage tended to be a leisurely affair. Heavy lorries were low geared with a maximum legal top speed of 20 mph, although some were capable of reaching 32 to 38 mph depending on the model and gearing. In 1957 this longstanding 20 mph limit was abolished, permitting a heavy goods vehicle to travel at 30 mph on a single carriageway road and 40 mph on an unrestricted dual carriageway. By then an improved road network was coming into being. Many trunk routes had been made into dual carriageways and the first lengths of Motorways were under construction. The raising of the speed limit and an impending better road

Lancashire United Transport (LUT) served several districts in mid and southern areas of the county and grew to be the largest independently owned bus company in England. Its main make of bus for most of its existence was the Guy Arab with Gardner engine. Because LUT operated into Patricroft and its main depot was but a few miles away from Barton Hall, Gardner's at various times used LUT buses for development work and trials. Not every LUT bus was a Guy and a batch of Dennis double deckers, one of which is shown here, was supplied in 1949. Gardner 6LW engines powered these Dennis Lancet buses.

CN. 116

This consignment of 10 Guy single deck buses was part of the government driven exporting campaign of the post-war years.
The vehicles were supplied to Koyna Bus Services in Nairobi, and were fitted with Gardner 5LW power units.

Gardner's spare parts policy was to provide service exchange for certain components. This extended to fuel injectors, or "sprayers" as they were always known at Barton Hall. This early 1960s advertisement was for a works reconditioned sprayer at 10/6d., equivalent to the princely sum of £0.53 today, with a used sprayer taken in part exchange.

network made the need for a more powerful Gardner engine option imperative. Transport bosses were demanding shorter journey times from drivers and this could only be achieved by higher power outputs. Ironically this was an era of strong trades unionism in road haulage and BRS had been instrumental in encouraging this by agreeing with the unions a daily maximum mileage for drivers. When more powerful engines became available this maximum distance was increased slightly. However, many drivers got their revenge by being able to get from café to café quicker as well as satisfying bosses because their daily productivity mileages were greater. But they did not actually lose out as they still booked similar totals of duty hours as previously, and of course, wages were calculated on hourly rates.

By the mid-fifties ten years had elapsed since the end of World War Two. During this period there had been a noticeable trend away from engine series with variable numbers of cylinders. For commercial vehicles applications either four or six-cylinder units were preferred, although Gardner's would remain unique among engine suppliers by offering its five-cylinder LW type for lorries and buses until the late sixties. This preference for bigger engines was also reflected in sales of Gardner six and eight-cylinder marine, rail, and industrial power units. Hugh Gardner recognised that the market was changing and responded by developing a new six-cylinder engine of 150 bhp, with assistance from his brother John. Like the famous 4LK design of the thirties the Gardner 6LX, as it was designated, was available only in one format.

The North American commercial vehicles market was notoriously difficult for British manufacturers to break into. There were several reasons for this including the completely different vehicle design philosophies followed on either side of the Atlantic Ocean. Another reason was the adherence of American and Canadian operators to gasoline fuelled trucks and buses until relatively recent times because gasoline (or petrol) was so cheap there. Some limited success was gained in Canada with diesel engines supplied by Gardner, Leyland Motors, and AEC, but they could not break the prominence in the proprietary diesel engines market enjoyed by Cummins and Caterpillar. Until Mack trucks perfected its own Maxidyne diesel engines some Gardner units were fitted and this typical articulated outfit for Shell Oil Company of Canada was badged "Mack Gardner".

ABOVE: Country Freight
Lines of Vancouver operated
this Canadian Kenworth
six-wheeler with a Gardner
6LW engine.
(Photo: Dominion Photo Co.)

RIGHT: The operator of this
Hayes Anderson six-wheeler
was not recorded, but a
Gardner engine sump is
visible in this ground level
shot. Under close
examination the number
plate reveals that the vehicle
was registered in the
Canadian state of
British Columbia.
(Photo: Dominion Photo Co.)

One American operator keen to try Gardner engines was Turner Transfer Inc. of Greensboro, North Carolina. These photographs show a 6LW being installed into a Mack EHU tractive unit, and the finished truck. The Gardner engine replaced a Mack petrol unit of 354 cubic inches which produced 115 bhp at 2,850 rpm, and 254 lbs.ft. of torque. The 6LW was of similar power at 112 bhp, but at 358 lbs. ft. torque gave an increase of 41%, and improved fuel consumption into the bargain. A Gardner badge is prominent, as is the notice on the fuel tank to use diesel fuel rather than gasoline that the driver would be more used to.

Turner Transfer also took delivery of Gardner 8LWs and one was fitted under the huge bonnet of this Mack LJT. It replaced a Mack petrol unit of 707 cubic inches rated at 171 bhp at 2,200 rpm, and maximum torque of 520 lbs. ft. An 8LW automotive unit normally produced 150 bhp at 1,700 rpm and 478 lbs. ft. of torque in the 1950s. One reason Turner Transfer was keen to use Gardner engines was a connection with Westfield Transport of Mansfield, England, and both companies used the same logo of two men carrying a beam for part of their respective vehicles' livery. Guy Turner visited Westfield Transport and was impressed by the fuel economy of their Gardner powered Scammells. Another American truck builder to fit Gardner 8LW engines at the request of Turner Transfer was a small company called Corbitt.

While the 6LX was based on the LW series and any improvements incorporated therein down the years it was in effect a brand new design. For the Gardner 6LX the 6 inches piston stroke of the LW was retained but the cylinder bore was widened by ½ inch to 4¾ inches. This resulted in a total swept volume of 10.45 litres and the traditional Gardner maximum governed speed of 1,700 rpm was retained. The first production 6LX, serial number 117100, was tested rather inappropriately on 1st April 1958 and it embodied time-honoured Gardner features: – aluminium alloy crankcase; wide bearings; an unhardened crankshaft machined all over; chain driven camshaft; long stroke with lengthy connecting rods for minimising piston side thrust; pistons with

long, relieved, skirts; hemispherical combustion chambers with centrally positioned sprayers; and masked inlet valves for inducing air swirling. For this engine the fuel injection rate and timing was exclusive to Gardner's own injection pump cambox which had a special load responsive governor.

It had become standard procedure for other engine manufacturers to prove new designs by subjecting them to intensive testing in vehicles. Sales brochures boasted how many miles they had achieved under the most arduous conditions of round the clock running seven days a week. There was none of this at Barton Hall Works for the new 6LX. Gardner's research department assembled a prototype 6LX and its design was so good very little further develop-

ment was needed. This knowledge, expertise, and confidence of Hugh and John Gardner resulted in the initial batch of twenty-five production 6LXs being put through the works in February 1958 after only a very short period of prototype testing.

However, the Gardner 6LX was an instant success and achieved a miserly fuel consumption figure of 0.330 lbs./bhp/hour, – a world record for a diesel engine of this type and size. Its thermal efficiency was also remarkably good at 39.75%. And engine torque was maintained within a phenomenally low 5% of the maximum figure, (485 lbs.ft. for road going applications at 1,000 to 1,100 rpm), throughout the crankshaft revolutions range. Moreover, the overall dimensions of a Gardner 6LX engine were the

same as a 6LW so a new and more powerful unit could easily replace a 6LW without the need for chassis modifications.

Most other engine makers strove for a 'flat torque curve' across the revolutions range like Gardner's, but tended to achieve rather 'peaky' ones like small mountains. Optimistically they often referred to this 'as good torque back-up' but it would have been more accurate for them to describe it as 'torque fall-off' at high engine speeds. Constant torque is important for a lorry driver because it reduces the number of gear changes he needs to make during a journey. This in turn saves wear and tear on a vehicle's engine, clutch, and transmission. Also, and most importantly it gives lower fuel consumption because the engine is able to operate effectively at fewer revs.

The connection between Turner Transfer and Westfield was the transport of hosiery machinery. By the early 1950s most British hosiery manufacturers were using imported American machines and Guy Turner's company packed and crated the equipment in the U.S.A. and hauled it to the port of embarkation. The first imported machine arrived in England in January 1948. On arriving at Liverpool Westfield Transport collected the crates and transported them to their destination. To prevent problems of incompatibility of crate sizes to trailers there was close co-operation between both hauliers. This rather dingy photograph of Westfield Transport's Gardner 6LW powered Scammell was taken in 1951, and even at that time the company undertook European journeys.
(Photo: Westfield Transport Ltd.)

TOP: Gardner marine engines were used in luxury yachts and launches owned by several wealthy and prominent people. The Sheik of Kuwait's launch, M.L. "Tarrad" had twin 6LW marine units fitted. It was photographed during trials shortly after completion.

ABOVE: Marine versions of Gardner 6LX engines were produced in due course and used in inshore and harbour craft such as one of the Plymouth ferries, "Western Belle", seen here.

ABOVE: Atkinson Lorries (1933) Ltd. was re-organised in that year and started building diesel-engined vehicles. It had previously built steam wagons and carried out chassis modifications such as 4 to 6-wheeler conversions on other makes of lorry. Atkinsons were only assembled in small numbers until the early 1950s, but they were solid and well made and used Gardner engines. Atkinson cab styles did not alter too much from inception until the 1960s. These three 4-wheelers were supplied to Gracey Brothers Ltd., Northern Ireland. Photographed laden with fruit; they had Gardner 4LW engines installed.

ABOVE: A post-war maximum weight 4-wheeler lorry could legally gross 12 tons until 1955, when it became 14 tons. Gardner 4LW units at 75 bhp (slightly uprated 'K' series LW engines) were deemed powerful enough for such weights and this ERF milk tanker had such a specification when it entered service. For many years similar types of lorries from ERF and Atkinson had identical drivelines of Gardner engines, David Brown gearboxes, and Kirkstall rear axles, but ERF tended to be more adventurous in cab styling compared with its erstwhile rival.

ABOVE: Bedford is not usually a marque associated with fitting Gardner engines, but some dealers would fit them at operators' requests. In 1953 Bedford started to move up the weight range with its "Big Bedford" S Types for 7 tons payload, illustrated here. At that date Bedford did not produce its own diesel engine, the options being either a 6-cylinder petrol unit, which was costly to run, or a proprietary Perkins R6 indirect injection diesel. The Perkins engine was a new design and proved to be troublesome and unreliable in service. Bedford introduced its own diesel engine in 1958. Allen's, one of Gardner's local haulage contractors, arranged for Blake's Motors of Manchester, Bedford dealers for the area, to install a Gardner 4LW unit in their new Bedford S Type in early 1957.

ABOVE: Complementing the Bedford S Type seven tonner was a range of normal control five tonners known as Bedford A Types. These had replaced the tough little O Types in the early fifties. Engine options for A Types were Bedford's 6-cylinder petrol unit, or a Perkins P6. These Perkins units were good engines, but some operators wished for something even better. Enfield Rolling Mills of Bradford operated this Bedford A Type, new in 1957, with a Gardner 4LK engine. It was photographed with a load of aluminium ingots, probably destined for the aluminium foundry at Barton Hall.

ABOVE: Here is the M.V. "Kusa", built by James A. Silver Ltd. of Rosneath for the British Tanker Co. Ltd. She was a refrigerated fish carrier 83 feet long and with twin Gardner 8L3 marine main engines with direct drive reverse gears. A Gardner 2LW auxiliary generating unit of 10 Kilowatts was also installed. A speed of 10.84 knots was achieved on trials. (Photo: James Hall Ltd., Greenock)

LEFT: This little mooring launch was built for The Anglo-Iranian Oil Company Limited (now BP) and had a Gardner 6LW marine engine installed. (Photo: Waverley Photographic, Barnstaple)

RIGHT: The pilot boat "Seniceva" was built by W.R. Carpenter & Co. (Fiji) Ltd. in 1953. Her main propulsion unit was a Gardner 6L3 marine engine, number 80945.

BELOW RIGHT: Trinity House was the organisation responsible for the numerous lighthouses and lightships located around the shores of the British Isles. With powerful lights and foghorns capable of being seen and heard from several miles distant they needed reliable engines to provide continuous service throughout the year. Gardner's supplied Trinity House with engines from the early years of the twentieth century. This lightship was one of the larger types and was moored off the Devon coast. (Photo: Nicholas Horne Ltd., Totnes)

TOP LEFT: Engine room view of a lightship with at least two Gardner engines for each individual piece of equipment to provide a safeguard against complete failure in the event of a breakdown. Clearly in view are three 1L2 generating sets for the light, and two 5LWs for the foghorn. The policy followed by Trinity House for three lighting sets was to have one engine in use, one on standby, and one under repair or overhaul. Some lightships also had a fourth 1L2, and this was such an engine room, with the silencer for the extra unit just visible on the extreme right of the picture. Lightships are static vessels with no propulsion engines. (Photo: Nicholas Horne Ltd., Totnes)

BOTTOM LEFT: The prestigious order for Gardner LW marine engines from the Royal National Lifeboat Institution received in 1954 came about partly from pressure exerted from fishermen who normally constituted a lifeboat's crew. Many of these seafarers depended upon Gardner reliability daily and had great respect for Barton Hall's products. In this tranquil scene the lifeboat "George Urie Scott" approaches a fishing vessel. (Photo: Copyright of Aberdeen Journals Limited.)

It was quite common then for competitors to obtain their rivals' engines for stripping down so they could be evaluated and any secrets discerned. Gardner's were aware that every competing manufacturer had acquired at least one 6LW for examination and testing. To Gardner's credit never once did they dissect any other companies' engines. But the day following the announcement of the 6LX an official order was received from Leyland Motors for one engine. The chit was returned the same day "with regrets that the supply situation was difficult". Leyland's engineers got hold of a 6LX some months later from Scammell, which was then fully owned by Leyland Motors.

The Gardner 6LX '150' became an additional engine in the sales catalogue and it was an immediate favourite with eight-wheeler, and maximum weight tractive unit lorry purchasers. Industrial adaptations for compressors, generators, cranes, excavators, and civil engineering plant soon became available. Passenger chassis makers such as Bristol fitted some 6LXs in conventional layout buses and Daimler chose the 6LX engine to power its new rear-engined bus introduced in 1959. In the year 1960 two more versions of the Gardner 6LX design were announced. These were a horizontal 6HLX for underfloor applications in coaches and railcars, and a 6LX marine type. This Gardner 6LX marine engine was particularly suitable for smaller fishing boats, high-class pleasure craft, and the new generation of RNLI self-righting lifeboats.

Many of the design features used in the Gardner 6LX were incorporated into the long-serving industrial and marine L3 series of engines. In late 1960 the opportunity was taken to further modernise these power units and they were gradually replaced with six or eight-cylinder L3B versions,

Photographed on the River Thames near Chiswick in about 1960, the M.T. "Baba" had a Gardner 8L3 engine installed. "Baba" was a typical pleasure cruiser from that era, of the sort used along the Thames westwards from Tower Bridge. (Photo: Wakefields Ltd., Chiswick)

By the 1960s it was calculated that approximately one third of Great Britain's inshore fishing boats had Gardner engines. This tradition had begun with 'M' series engines in the early 1900s. As new vessels were constructed through the years, the latest types of Gardner engines were installed. The M.F.V. "Gleaner" had a Gardner 6LX marine engine with 3:1 reduction and reverse gear. (Photo: Van Hallan, Twickenham)

which retained the cylinder dimensions of the earlier range. L3B engines were considerably more powerful than L3 types. The largest available, an eight cylinder 8L3B, could produce up to 260 bhp at 1,300 rpm ensuring its continued popularity with fishing fleet owners and shunting locomotive builders. The RNLI chose to equip each of two new 71 feet long ocean patrol boats with twin marine 8L3B main propulsion engines.

The last Gardner L3 engine was an eight-cylinder version, serial number 132132, which was tested on 6th December 1961. There was an overlap period of twelve months when both L3 and L3B ranges were produced. The first Gardner L3B was an eight-cylinder engine, serial number 126600, and it was fired-up on 30th November 1960.

Gardner 8L3, then 8L3B engines were very popular with fishing boat owners because they gave lengthy service lives before requiring overhauling. They were also reliable and economical, with the former trait being essential in treacherous sea conditions. With an overall length of 65ft. the fishing boat "Pilot Us" relied on a Gardner 8L3B unit. She was built by James Noble Ltd. and owned by Messrs. Bogg & Cotes of Bridlington.

In the year 1962 there was another reorganization of the subsidiary Norris, Henty, & Gardners Ltd. For many years before customers had been receiving engines on an allocation basis and had to wait at least six months for delivery. Some of those ordering the largest marine engines were forced to wait two years, and then only after paying a 10% deposit with their order. Hugh and John Gardner preferred to deal directly with their Director counterparts at chassis builders like ERF, Foden, and Atkinson. Norris, Henty, & Gardners handled all export, marine, rail traction, and other industrial sales outlets. This long-standing company was replaced by Gardner Engines (Sales) Ltd., which was still a separate organisation, but with its head office at Patricroft. Latterly Norris, Henty, & Gardners had been located at 52, Grosvenor

TOP: The "St. Giles" was a bucket dredger built in 1958 for the Admiralty. She had a Gardner 4LW auxiliary engine driving a 20 Kilowatts dynamo. (Photo: W. Ralston Ltd.)

ABOVE: A Huwood-Hudswell Tandem mine locomotive prepared for display at the Festival of Britain in 1951. It was composed of two single locomotives each powered by a Gardner 6LW engine, set to produce 102 bhp at 1,700 rpm. At the time this machine was the heaviest and most powerful mine locomotive built for service in Great Britain.

Gardens, London S.W.1 and this was replaced with a London sales office at Brixton Hill. Another branch office was retained at Glasgow.

Having full order books for several months ahead is the aim of any manufacturing company and Gardner's had been in that enviable position for thirty years by the early sixties. Annual average production was around 4,600 complete engines, (see Appendix D), the majority being six-cylinder units. Further buildings and extensions had increased the total floor area of workshops and foundries at Barton Hall to 48,000 square yards. (It is recalled that a new spare parts bay was erected in 1954 using a second hand building bought in East Anglia because of a shortage of steel). With third generation Gardner family members holding shares and because several lots of death duties had been imposed through the years it was necessary to release ordinary shares onto the stock exchange. Nevertheless, over 30% of shares were still retained by Gardner family members, with some 20% also being held by loyal friends. The firm was recording solid financial results annually and could approach its centenary confidently.

In addition to low height mine locomotives Hunslet built shunting engines such as this with a Gardner 8L3 power unit. It was operated by the Mersey Docks and Harbour Board. The standard rail traction engine output for an 8L3 was 153 bhp at 1,200 rpm. Electric starting was usually supplied, but a compressed air starter motor was an optional choice for the user.

CHAPTER
8

A CENTENARY
IN A TIME OF CHANGE

After a rather hectic decade in the fifties, the early sixties saw Gardner's being run by a trinity of Hugh Gardner, his brother John, and Frank Wilkinson, a chartered accountant, who of course was son of Elizabeth Gardner. Hugh was still wary of "outsiders" being appointed to the Board by institutional shareholders, so, as and when vacancies for Directors arose selected dutiful employees filled them. They were representative of different sections of the firm, being members of staff or from the sales division. Typical of these appointments were Eric Bradshaw, Gordon Thompstone, and Eric Todd, all elected to the Board in 1956. They took little part in decision-making but were representative of so many others who did sterling work in various departments to maintain Gardner's reputation.

To be a Gardner's Director was of course a status symbol. They were not provided with company cars or similar perks, but they could enjoy a concessionary priced lunch everyday! Board meetings took place every half year and Directors were given slips of paper informing them which items on the agenda they should either propose or second. It might sound bizarre but the system worked. In the unlikely event of anything being queried Hugh Gardner would retort, " I am the largest employer

ESTABLISHED 1868

GARDNER

L. GARDNER & SONS L^{TD}

MANUFACTURERS OF
DIESEL ENGINES
AUTOMOTIVE, RAIL TRACTION,
MARINE and INDUSTRIAL

LONDON OFFICE
GARDNER ENGINES (SALES) LTD
ABFORD HOUSE, WILTON ROAD, S.W.I.
TELEPHONES: TATE GALLERY 3315-6
CABLES & TELEGRAMS: GARDIESEL, LONDON, S.W.I.

DIRECTORS
J. H. S. GARDNER
J. K. GARDNER
F. G. WILKINSON
W. G. THOMPSTONE
E. A. TODD

SECRETARY
F. G. WILKINSON

YOUR REF......................

OUR REF......................

CABLES & TELEGRAMS:
GARDWORKS, ECCLES, MANCHESTER

TELEPHONES:
ECCLES 2201-8

REGISTERED OFFICE:

BARTON HALL ENGINE WORKS.

PATRICROFT,

ECCLES. MANCHESTER

.....................19

A Gardner's letterhead from the mid-60s and over the years it can be seen how letterhead styles altered and were simplified. However, the distinctive Gardner script logo was always retained and it was an instantly recognisable symbol identifying Gardner agents and repairers throughout the world. The logo was introduced in the early 1900s and it is attributed to a draughtsman at Barton Hall whose name has been lost in the mists of time.

others before him, Paul sometimes had problems working alongside his uncle, so his niche was to oversee engine installations in new chassis designs at lorry and passenger vehicles builders. Paul also assisted his father in streamlining the firm's spare parts supply and distribution operation. He was also responsible for the firm's service garage.

While it would not be entirely accurate to say that Hugh Gardner ran the company 'single-handedly' his management style was rather autocratic, and to some extent this was reflected in the relationships Gardner's had with customers.

The pioneering LW engine series had spurred commercial vehicles operators into demanding Gardner engines and launched the Patricroft firm on its way to greater prosperity in the early thirties. Because Gardner's were not chassis makers they needed outlets for engines and in particular lorry builders ERF and Atkinson achieved great success by fitting Gardner engines. The same applied to passenger vehicles made by Bristol, Guy, and Daimler. But Gardner's never had comfortable associations with the majority of chassis builders. This was partly because of constant shortages of

of labour in Eccles; I've got a twelve months order book, and I make a respectable profit. Where am I wrong?"

Running a company in such a way might be questionable but the fact remains that Hugh's 6LX engine design was brilliant, unbeatable at home and abroad.

With Gardner's approaching centenary in 1968 it was appropriate to reflect on the firm's considerable achievements during its existence. It had won an envied reputation for engineering excellence in manu-

facturing diesel engines. Reliability, longevity, and fuel economy; - they are three traits that will forever be associated with the Gardner name. There remained a strong Gardner family presence controlling the direction of the company with Hugh Gardner as Chairman. In 1966 he was joined on the Board by his nephew Paul Gardner, John's son and a great-grandson of the founder. Paul had served his time and passed all his engineering exams to become a chartered engineer. He was also a competent draughtsman. Like

TOP LEFT, BOTTOM LEFT & RIGHT: One interesting car engine replacement was the fitting of a Gardner 4LK 'car' unit into John Gardner's Jaguar XK150. This particular Jaguar model with 3.8 litre dohc petrol engine was a much sought after sports car and the diesel conversion was rather a tight squeeze under the bonnet, as can be judged from these photographs. William Lyons (later Sir William), the genius behind the Jaguar marque, took a test drive in the Gardner powered car but was not too impressed by its reduced performance. However, fuel economy was outstanding with a certified and verified 90.85 mpg being achieved in a Mobil Economy Run, a popular event of the 1950s and 60s.

engines to fulfil orders and also because the family insisted on its products being installed properly. Gardner's believed that if left to their own devices, chassis assemblers would skimp on radiators, silencers and exhaust systems, air cleaners, and engine mountings. All these could impair an engine's performance and harm Gardner's reputation. One customer refused to fit oil coolers and consequently had its engine allocation reduced until it complied. So there was no love lost between most chassis manufacturers and Gardner's, and matters became worse when Barton Hall accepted the first orders from Seddon of Oldham despite increasing demands from regular clients.

Daimler had a good reputation for buses and eventually produced its own diesel engine. To promote this power unit fleet operators were informed that Gardner engines were in short supply and only Daimler's would be used. In the year 1951 Daimler asked Gardner's to take back ninety-two 6LWs, which they willingly did, and charged the Coventry firm handsomely for work that was necessary to convert them to another chassis maker's specification. The Daimler diesel engine was never really successful and was quietly dropped after a few years. Thereafter Gardner power units were usually fitted into Daimler buses.

It was commonly believed that a 6LW, for example, was the same for every road going application. In fact there were numerous versions. Some chassis required a centre sump, others either a forward or rear sump. Similarly there were variations in flywheels for different clutches, or fluid flywheels for pre-selector transmissions. Add onto these various configurations of air intakes; exhaust manifolds, crankcase endplates and engine mountings. Scammell lorries needed modified crankcases and options were available for single or twin cylinder exhausters, air compressors, hydraulic power steering pumps, dynamos or alternators. So a Bristol 6LW was quite different from an ERF 6LW, but both were basically 6LWs. Chassis builders would place orders for two hundred engines of a particular specification, say for arguments sake, with flywheels for 15-inch clutches. Woe betides them if partway through the contract they changed to 16-inch clutches.

A view in the engine room of the "Southern Cross", a Sydney registered vessel with twin Gardner 8L3B marine main engines and 4LW auxiliary set.

Gardner's would inform them in no uncertain terms that they would be charged for the scrap value of the unused items. This policy did not endear these chassis assemblers to Gardner's, but if they wanted engines there were no alternative proprietary engine makers in the fifties. Both AEC and Leyland Motors competed in most of the same engine markets as Gardner's but supplying competing chassis makers with power units was not their core business. Of the cheaper lorry makers such as Bedford and Dodge, optional engines from Leyland and AEC were fitted in some of these chassis to tempt prospective buyers who wanted something better than a Perkins R6, for instance, but this had no impact on Gardner's. Some large fleets had AEC or Leyland power units in Atkinsons and Guys for the sake of spares compatibility with larger numbers of AECs or Leylands already in service. For example, AEC powered Atkinsons were sold to Whitbread and Harold Wood, both of which ran large quantities of AECs. The biggest lorry fleet of all in the fifties and sixties, namely that of BRS, ordered Bristol eight-wheelers with Leyland engines, and various other makes, including Seddon, with either Leyland or AEC power units for the sake of standardisation. After Leyland Motors bought a substantial share holding in Foden it allowed them to use its engines as an option.

But by the early sixties the situation was altering. The American engine maker Cummins was beginning to make inroads into the British market and had established its own manufacturing facility at Shotts. It is firmly believed that this initiative to build a factory in Great Britain was taken after a

TOP LEFT:
The M.B. "Venus" undergoing trials off Fraserburgh in August 1971. She had a Gardner 8L3B engine installed. (Photo: John S. Pirie)

BOTTOM LEFT:
By the time this photograph was taken in 1971 many Scottish fishing boat skippers had used Gardner engines in the preceding 64 years. The first recorded Gardner installation into a Scottish vessel had taken place in 1907 when the "Maggie Janes" received a 55 bhp 3KM paraffin engine. A modern version of a traditional fishing boat was the "Faithful", seen here, and she had considerably more power and speed than her ancestor, courtesy of a Gardner 8L3B marine engine. (Photo: John S. Pirie)

In November 1971 the M.B. "Silver Bell" was undergoing engine trials off the coat of North Eastern Scotland. She had a Gardner 8L3B engine, which by then was the popular choice for all new fishing boats of this type. "Silver Bell" was built by James Noble Ltd. of Fraserburgh.
(Photo: John S. Pirie)

senior Cummins executive named Sebastian visited Barton Hall Works in 1957. He had requested an appointment with the Gardner family and the discussions of that meeting have never been disclosed. Mr Sebastian was given a tour of the works and it is reasonable to assume that after seeing how labour intensive engine building was at Patricroft he concluded that Gardner's could never cope with additional demands.

Hugh Gardner rarely left Barton Hall except to take two weeks annual leave touring Scottish fishing ports where he could happily chat to fishermen about Gardner engines. He also visited the Commercial Vehicle Show which took place in alternate years at London and Glasgow. At the 1964 event Hugh was surprised to see a dearth of Gardner engines on the displays mounted by ERF, Atkinson, Foden, and Guy. In fact none of these traditional Gardner users had any such engines in their chassis. There were just a few in vehicles on body builder's stands. Replacing Gardner engines were a plethora of Cummins NHE 180 units. Visitors to Gardner's own display were asking how long they would survive. "Just wait and see" was the reply given by Gardner's salesmen.

The various chassis makers thought that at last they had broken Gardner's stranglehold on them and could barely contain their glee at this prospect. But it was short-lived when operators proved they preferred increased payload (a Cummins NHE 180 was heavier than a Gardner 6LX) and the 15% better fuel consumption of their favourite engine. The Managing Directors of the chassis builders were forced to return cap-in-hand to Barton Hall for Gardner engines. Their excuse for choosing Cummins show exhibits was a shortage of Gardners. After this almost all of them charged a premium of up to £1,000 for a Gardner powered chassis. Again this was done to encourage alternative engine manufacturers and this surcharge represented about 17% of the total chassis price, which was a

lot of money in the mid-sixties. Incidentally, although Rolls Royce had introduced an automotive diesel engine shortly after the Second World War it was troublesome and never gained the reputation of a Rolls Royce petrol engine. It took them nearly twenty-five years to bring their design to fruition so that it finally became a serious competitor to Gardner's.

In spite of these machinations by the chassis makers, operators remained loyal to Gardner's. Back in 1931 and the infancy of diesel propulsion for commercial vehicles, demand from lorry owners and passenger transport authorities had created the Gardner legend. But the sixties was a decade of tremendous changes in road transport and inevitably these affected Gardner's considerably.

The quarter century from the end of the Second World War to 1970 can rightly be regarded as a halcyon period of British lorry and bus manufacturing. There were very few European and foreign vehicles in service in Great Britain and prospective purchasers had several marques and numerous models to choose from. During these years the larger British companies designed and produced commercial vehicles equal to any made elsewhere in the world, and in many instances they were superior. Export markets were thriving and while it is true many member countries of the British Commonwealth imported these lorries and buses, several European and South American states with no loyalty engendered by kith and kin willingly bought British. Gardner's were an integral and important part of this successful major British Industry.

In the early 1960s Gardner 6LX '150' engines had become very popular with operators of maximum weight rigid and articulated lorries made by Atkinson, ERF, Foden, Guy, Scammell, and Seddon. However, the archrivals in these particular markets, Leyland Motors and AEC, had merged into an uneasy alliance. Both of them had moved ahead in the power stakes once more with engines capable of 200 bhp, (Leyland's P.680), and 192 bhp, (AEC's 2AV690). Every few months witnessed a new section of Motorway being opened and transport managers were expecting drivers to reduce journey times.

Two totally unrelated happenings in the mid-sixties gave road haulage a massive boost and changed the

This smart looking vessel is R.S.C. "Nivanga", built in 1962 by Hongkong & Whampoa Dock Co. Ltd. She was the Resident Commissioner's Ship of the Gilbert and Ellice Islands and had twin Gardner 8L3B main engines with a couple of 6LW marine auxiliary sets. Dodwell & Company, Gardner's distributors in Hong Kong won the order for the engines.

face of the industry. Firstly, in 1963, the infamous Beeching Report on the railways was accepted and thousands of miles of rail track were earmarked for closure and lifting. In the next few years when many communities became impossible to reach by railway, vast tonnages of

Thos. Smith (Rodley) Ltd. built this Smith M.E.I. Truck Mounted Crane on a Foden six-wheeler chassis. The crane had a lifting capacity of 22.5 tons at 10 ft. radius and it was driven by a Gardner 5LW engine. The Foden had a 6LW power unit and the mobile crane was lifting the top section of a tower crane into position.
(Photo: Leslie Studios)

goods were transferred to the roads. Secondly, changes resulting from the 1964 Construction and Use Regulations gave articulated lorries a significant payload advantage over eight-wheelers. Not only did this hasten the demise of these vehicles as flagships of British road transport fleets and their replacement by artics, it also altered the economics of freight carriage. Consequently much of the remaining rail traffic became too costly and this was eventually lost to road transport.

Because a new, post-1964 articulated lorry could have a maximum gross weight of 32 tons (although resulting from a quirk of the legislation 30 tons gross weight became more common until 1968), additional engine power was required. Hugh Gardner went to his drawing board and retuned his 6LX design to produce the Gardner 6LXB which was rated at180 bhp at 1,850 rpm. The torque output was 536 lbs.ft. at 1,000 to 1,100 rpm. But this was not just a simple re-working of an existing engine because fuel economy was even better at an outstanding 0.328 lb/bhp/hr. Thermal efficiency was recorded at 40% and this figure had never been achieved before with an engine of this size anywhere in the world.

The first testing of a Gardner 6LXB was on 18th July 1966 when engine number 153276 was started-up in the experimental department at Barton Hall. Acceptance from all the chassis builders was immediate, but it was not until the following year that anything more than a trickle of these engines started to leave Patricroft. When time permitted marine and industrial versions of 6LXBs were assembled. Such was the incessant demand for Gardner engines that the 4LK was discontinued along with some of the smaller LW marine units. In the case of the 4LK more powerful and much cheaper automotive engines from other suppliers such as Perkins had superseded it. While such engines had nowhere near the fuel economy and quality of the revolutionary little Gardner, mass producers at the cheaper end of the market made the lorries needing this size of engine.

In the year 1968 L. Gardner & Sons Ltd. celebrated its proud centenary. One hundred years of progress, innovation and achievement. True pioneers of direct diesel

injection engines for road vehicles. In typical Gardner's style there was only a minor celebration, but testimony to their success was unceasing demand for engines. Much of Barton Hall's output was destined for automotive usage with five main vertical types listed. These were 4LW, 5LW, 6LW, 6LX, and 6LXB providing power outputs from 80 bhp to 180 bhp. Horizontal versions were mainly restricted to six-cylinder units. The most popular rail traction power units were six and eight-cylinder L3Bs with a maximum of 260 bhp available. Various marine and industrial engines were also made ranging from 56 to 230 bhp

for numerous applications. In this centenary year it was calculated that one third of the British registered fishing fleet was Gardner powered.

As the company embarked on its second century there was a shortage of skilled tradesmen and engineers in the Manchester area. Weekly advertisements in the local press notified job seekers of scores of vacancies at Barton Hall. But the well-tried and traditional manufacturing processes remained sacrosanct at Gardner's. The machine shops worked shifts, but only daytime workers assembled engines. Every engine was tested before it left the works and it had to be signed-off by a Test Superintendent. Even with

An internal view of the assembly area of Diesel Services Pty. Ltd., Melbourne. Atkinson lorries are being assembled after being shipped to Australia in chassis knocked down (CKD) format. Gardner engines, axles, springs, gearboxes, and wheels can be seen. Interestingly the fuel tank has been mounted behind the cab of the six-wheeler, rather than on the chassis rail, indicating that the lorry was destined for a hard life working over rough terrain.

Another Smiths (Rodley) machine dating from 1964. It was a Smith 26 Excavator Crane fitted with a 0.75 cubic yards drag shovel bucket and was driven by a Gardner 5LW engine.

the firm being able to sell more engines than could be produced there was no corner cutting and the highest quality was maintained.

In particular orders for 6LXB engines were excellent. These units had become very popular in rear-engined buses which had revived the stagnant double decker market. Their front entrance layout made one man operating an attractive proposition for municipal authorities and independent companies alike. Plenty of Gardner powered buses were entering service with the prestigious London Transport fleet. For virtually all of its existence this huge undertaking had relied on AEC, and to a lesser extent, Leyland products. The merger of those two incompatible organisations in 1962 and their inability to work together harmoniously resulted in several marketing disasters of which the loss of London Transport's replacement business was only one. However, Gardner's benefited greatly from this.

This impressive drilling rig was driven by a Gardner 6LX engine with an industrial rating of 119 bhp at 1,400 rpm. It was carried on a Foden eight-wheeler chassis which was also powered by a Gardner 6LX, but at the usual automotive output of 150 bhp. The rig was used for sinking building foundations and it was operated by McKinney Foundations Limited.

The ill-fated "St. Finbarr", a refrigerated stern trawler built by Ferguson Bros. Port Glasgow, Ltd. She was equipped with a Gardner 6L3B auxiliary generating set and her home port was Hull. After being at sea for 38 days a serious fire broke out on board the trawler early on Christmas Day 1966. The "St. Finbarr" was about 600 miles northwest of St. John's Newfoundland. Initial radio reports from a similar vessel, the "Sir Fred Parkes", which was standing by to assist, along with another Hull trawler "Orsino", stated that ten crew had been rescued, two were lost, and thirteen were unaccounted for. Later reports confirmed that the fire was still burning after 17 hours and that the "Orsino" had taken the "St. Finbarr" under tow, and her crew had rescued thirteen survivors and one body. By then the fire was confined to the fuel tanks, but in worsening weather the "Orsino" could only make 3 knots in heavy seas and she was heading for St. Anthony, N.F. The inferno eventually burned

itself out but the gallant "Orsino", still with "Sir Fred Parkes" standing by, was battling a 35-knot gale, snow, sleet, and rain. On 27th December it was reported at Hull that twelve crewmembers of the "St. Finbarr" were officially considered lost and there were thirteen named survivors, including the skipper, Captain Tom Sawyer. Later that same day, in appalling weather conditions the "Orsino" eventually lost her brave battle to bring the bodies of her fellow Hull trawler men to port and the "St. Finbarr" finally sunk some 14 miles north-north-east off Cape Bauld, at the northernmost point of Newfoundland. On Wednesday 28th December 1966, late in the evening, the "Orsino" arrived in St. John's N.F. harbour with thirteen survivors and the body of one crewmember of "St. Finbarr", the other eleven bodies going down with the trawler. Captain Sawyer reported hearing a few small explosions just before the devastating and tragic fire on his ship.

LEFT: With the impending gross weight increases to 30/32 tons for articulated lorries applicable from 1965, Gardner's returned to Parbold Hill on 28th September 1964 to test their 6LX 150 engine at higher weights. This Lancashire hill is 1 in 7 at its steepest and a couple of Atkinson Mark 1 tractive units tackled the ascent. One was a works demonstrator from nearby Walton-le-Dale; the other was a relatively new lorry from the fleet of Sutton & Sons of St. Helens. The demonstrator (being overtaken by a Mini) is seen leading Sutton's lorry, and then SDJ 44 nears the summit followed by a Jaguar and an elderly Foden. Needless to say the tests were successful and were deemed to have been completed with reserves of power to spare.

The clamour for even more power was unrelenting from lorry operators by the close of the sixties. AEC of Southall's biggest automotive engine, the AV760, reliably produced 226 bhp and had become the British Leyland Group's most popular high power unit after the disastrous failure of an under-developed AEC V8 design of 247 bhp. Both Cummins and Rolls Royce were competing strongly with Gardner's for orders from ERF, Foden, Atkinson, and Seddon

operators. These engine makers also had power units in the 220 bhp region. Nevertheless, Gardner's had an answer and what an astonishing one it was. In 1970 they announced their eight-cylinder 8LXB engine of 13.9 litres capacity and 240 bhp at 1,850 rpm. It retained all the features of 6LXB units, but of course had two additional cylinders. Previously most rival engine designers had dismissed the notion of an eight-cylinder commercial vehicle diesel engine as being too

heavy and too long. But the extensive use of light aluminium alloy by Gardner's made their 8LXB a practical proposition. The nine main bearings Gardner 8LXB 240 was a delightfully smooth engine and the Barton Hall firm was unique in offering a 'straight-eight' as a mainline British lorry power unit. Yes, 8LXBs were long, but twenty years previously when Gardner's had offered 8LW engines to chassis makers the eight-wheeler rigid lorry had reigned supreme. By 1970

RIGHT: Discussing the tests on Parbold Hill were John Gardner (left) and Alf Sutton. Sutton & Son of St. Helens was one of the largest privately owned road transport firms in the country in 1964 and operated a very large Gardner powered Atkinson fleet. Firms such as Sutton were loyal Gardner customers for decades and established successful and profitable businesses with Gardner products.

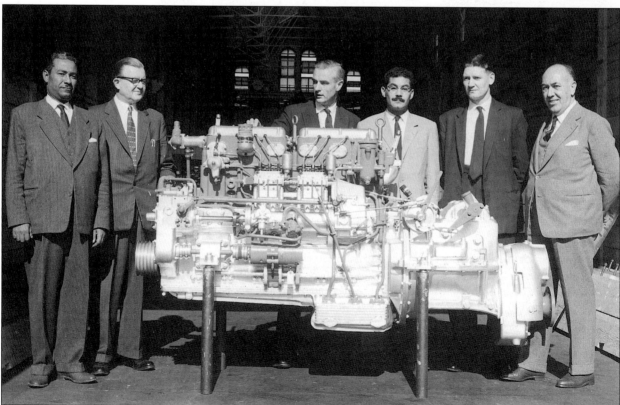

ABOVE: Over the years many visitors and delegations travelled to Barton Hall. One such visit took place on 3rd June 1963 when a party from the General Egyptian Organisation for Aquatic Resources had a tour of Gardner's Works. Pictured with a Gardner 6LX marine engine were left to right: Mr. A.W. El Hinnawi (delegation leader), Hugh Gardner, Dion Houghton, Capt. H.A. Ibrahim (U.A.R. Naval Forces), F. Brooks, and Mr. S. Monsif (commercial advisor).

tractive units ruled the roost and in such a lorry a long engine could happily protrude beyond the rear of the cab. With sleeper cabbed models becoming increasingly popular these deeper cabs actually covered the engine's length. However, the Gardner 8LXB option was expensive and while it became a popular choice for a few years in the 1970s the cost of specifying this engine eventually became prohibitive to the majority of lorry purchasers. One reason for the excessive cost of this unit was the

policy of chassis builders whereby they added an extra £1,000 to the engine price. This was done to make such a lorry unattractive and to promote the installation of Cummins and Rolls Royce units. Following established Gardner traditions marine and industrial 8LXB engines were introduced.

Further legislation enacted in 1968 amended the Construction and Use Regulations for lorries. It resulted in 32 tons gross weight on four axles for articulated vehicles becoming more feasible and from then on most

During the 1960s Penn Overland Tours Ltd advertised overland journeys to Australia by coach. This Guy Victory Trambus with Harrington Legionnaire bodywork was used for the round trip of approximately 20,000 miles. The journey took a scheduled 63 days each way. The Guy, new in 1965, was powered by a Gardner 6LX 150 engine and it completed three round trips to Australia in 13 months.

TOP LEFT: Demands for more power by customers led to the introduction of Gardner's 6LXB 180 in 1966, although very few entered service before 1967.

BOTTOM LEFT: Rapidly changing conditions in road transport soon meant that 180 bhp was believed insufficient for certain applications. Gardner's responded with an eight-cylinder 8LXB engine at 240 bhp, announced in 1970. At the time this power unit was easily the smoothest large diesel engine on the market.

heavy-duty artics entering service ran at this maximum weight. Included in this legislative package was a requirement for every new goods vehicle made from 1972 to be fitted with an engine giving a minimum power to weight ratio of 6 bhp per ton. To meet this requirement a re-rated version of Gardner's 6LXB was advertised. This produced 188 bhp, still at 1,850 rpm and with legal allowable tolerances was able to be marketed for 30 tons weight applications, which after 1972 became the new maximum for rigid eight-wheelers.

Commencing in the early 1970s there was an amazing and rapid decline in the fortunes of some of Great Britain's biggest commercial vehicle makers. To start with Gardner's were immune from these upheavals as their customers ensured a continuing demand for engines. Some chassis builders such as ERF and Seddon were gaining market share and because Gardner engines were still rationed, Cummins and Rolls Royce units increasingly powered many of these lorries. Other traditional Gardner users like Foden were experiencing difficulties and in 1970 Seddon had bought Atkinson. This particular takeover was very acrimonious and caused uncertainty among many loyal Atkinson operators. As much of Gardner's output went to lorry builders it could not remain immune from these events, and especially when

Whilst Gardner's centenary was a relatively low-key affair, some recognition and celebrations did take place. This was the occasion of a centenary dinner that took place on 6th September 1968. Gardner's long serving and senior management flank Hugh Gardner, centre, with brother John behind.

European and Scandinavian marques made rapid advances into the British market. Eventually all these changes which commenced in the mid-sixties and culminated in events during the seventies would have far-reaching consequences for Gardner's.

END OF AN ERA

Gardner's entered the 1970s with a distinguished history and unequalled reputation for the highest of engineering standards. Order books were full for months ahead and engines were strictly rationed by allocations to customers. The firm was prosperous and almost 3,000 employees were dependent on Barton Hall Works for their livelihoods. It was in-conceivable that by the end of the decade the company would lose its independence.

British road transport was revolutionised by various legislative changes introduced during the 1960s. Not least of these was the introduction of Operator's Licensing which opened-up the haulage market to newcomers and allowed established hauliers to expand more easily than had previously been possible. Consequently, this, and other legislation created a huge demand for new lorries and in particular maximum weight tractive units. Scandinavian and European truck makers had targeted the British market and timed their sales campaigns perfectly as home manufacturers struggled to meet orders. Scania, Volvo, Mercedes, and later DAF filled a void created by lengthening delivery times. At that

time, around 1970, none of these makes had engineering superior to most premium British lorries, but they did have better specifications for heavier gross weights and Motorway operations. They were fitted with powerful turbo-charged engines and multi-ratio gearboxes, with superior drivers' cabs. Continental cab designs were ideal for long distance duties, being comfortable and quiet. These "foreign" lorries were also supported by good after-sales service and potential customers were expertly courted by brilliant marketing campaigns.

In addition to placing "seed" models into large fleets, smaller firms were the main customers to begin with. Such operators were keen to expand but did not have sufficient purchasing power to enable them to circumvent the long waiting lists of British makers. However, they could be supplied with a Volvo or similar within a short time of placing an order. By the mid-seventies all the large continental marques were firmly established in Great Britain with ranges of excellent vehicles. By then they were often mechanically superior to certain home produced counterparts because the traditional domestic

market leaders were beset by troubles. Some very famous names had tarnished reputations because of failings resulting from industrial relations unrest, underdeveloped designs, and poor assembly quality. The latter problem was partly caused by a serious lack of investment by several firms in new, modern manufacturing machinery.

During this period of great change in the lorry market Gardner's was able to further consolidate its position as a supplier of passenger vehicles engines. The rear-engined, front entrance double decker had replaced all conventional designs. Daimler, Bristol, MCW and Dennis were particularly successful with their Gardner powered models ensuring steady demand for engines.

Gardner engines traditionally had been fitted into "gaffer's lorries"; that is such as ERF, Atkinson, Foden, and Guy. These were premium models and expensive to buy, but relatively cheap to maintain and run. They were designed for long operational lives but their cabs were rather basic, noisy, and un-comfortable. Even though all these makers and other Gardner's customers were working flat out to meet the demands in the early seventies, Cummins and Rolls Royce

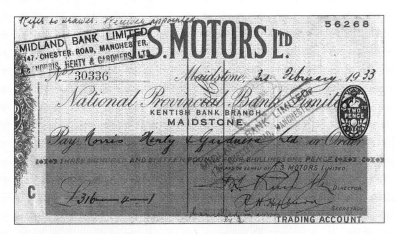

LEFT: Tilling Stevens of Maidstone, trading as T.S. Motors Ltd. produced some quite advanced vehicle designs in the 1930s, but as a company it was under-capitalised and struggled financially. These cheques from 31st January and 3rd February 1933 payable to Norris, Henty, & Gardners Ltd. "bounced" when presented at the bank. The total amount of almost £950 probably represented the cost of three Gardner 4LW engines.

BELOW: A display of Gardner and Lister marine diesel engines at Falmouth. Hawker Siddeley retained Gardner's as an autonomous division within its large group because there was little overlap between Gardner's range and those engines produced by the likes of Lister. Within a very few years of this photograph being taken the future for Gardner's became very uncertain.

GARDNER

ABOVE: In May 1990 a gathering of Seddon and Atkinson lorries took place at Belle Vue, Manchester. There were many examples present with Gardner engines and some were still in everyday service at 15 or more years old, confirming the Gardner reputation for longevity and reliability. Pictured here were Bostock's of Congleton Atkinson Raider four-wheeler, with 6LXB engine, and Woodcock's modified Atkinson Borderer articulated outfit, with 8LXB power unit. Bostock's ran a noted, immaculate, small fleet of lorries that were all Gardner powered. The artic was originally a 4x2 tractive unit and was later altered by adding an additional tag axle. (Photo: Author)

ABOVE: Gardner's own works transport fleet became famous in its own right in later years because of the age of its lorries. Most were twenty years or more old in the 1970s, proving the quality of Gardner engines and the lorries they were fitted in; namely Fodens, ERFs, and Atkinsons. As they were eventually withdrawn from service some were snapped up by preservationists. This Foden FG four-wheeler from about 1950 retained its correct livery when photographed at the Trans-Pennine Rally at Harrogate in August 1990. Sadly, some of these venerable old-timers have new liveries in preservation, changing their character entirely. (Photo: Author)

ABOVE: A White Road Commander which was one of two purchased by Travancore Transport, Melbourne. Each was powered by a Gardner 8LXB '240' engine, with 14-speed Spicer 1214-2A gearbox, and Rockwell rear bogie. This Australian transport company had a long association with Gardner engines dating back to 1937 and Thornycroft lorries with 4LW engines. For many years afterwards, Foden lorries were bought with Gardner units and this Gardner tradition carried on when Whites were procured. When this photograph was taken in October 1988 Travancore had been continuously operating Gardner powered lorries for over half a century. (Photo: Tony Petch)

ABOVE: At first glance this could be a typical British Atkinson eight-wheeler at work in the 1960s. However, the strange windscreens and "roo bar" identify the lorry as something a bit different. It was photographed on 21st May 1990 when the Atkinson was 26 years old, but the scene is testimony to the longevity of the chassis and its Gardner engine. When new in 1964 this Atkinson L1786XA, chassis number FCA8082, was fitted with a Gardner 6LX '150' engine and ZF 6-speed gearbox. Within two months the ZF transmission was replaced by a Fuller RT915, 9-speed range-change unit, as the lorry had to pull a trailer. Within three years the lorry had covered 387,000 miles, it was bought by Keith Flynn, and the engine was overhauled. Twenty three years on from then it was still soldering on after goodness knows how many miles in total. (Photo: Tony Petch)

Much was expected of the brand new Gardner 6LYT engine when it was introduced in late 1984. In truth the design was under-developed and the potential market for Gardner's engines had collapsed alarmingly. One of the first lorries to enter service, in 1985, with a 6LYT power unit was this Foden 6x4 artic, owned by Collier Waste Ltd. of Manchester.

Lowe Transport of Paddock Wood bought a few ERF tractive units with Gardner 6LYT engines for its refrigerated transport contract with the NAFFI. British military bases throughout Europe were serviced by these lorries, which with double drive rear bogies were over specified for their work. Alan Lowe sold his business to Turners (Soham) Ltd. and within twelve months these particular ERFs were disposed of, snapped up by fairground amusement caterers. D944 OKP was caught on film at Turners' Newmarket depot on a murky Sunday morning in September 1996. (Photo: Author)

GARDNER

Despite turbo-charged Gardner engines becoming available in the early 1980s, many bus operators were content with the proven Gardner 6LXB units and continued to specify them. This MCW Metrobus entered service in 1985 and was powered by a 6LXB. It was operated by Midland Bluebird in central Scotland. Production of new Gardner 6LXB engines ceased in 1992 when more stringent exhaust emissions legislation was enforced, and the 6LX design, which dated back to 1958 could no longer comply. The bus industry remains the biggest user of Gardner engines in Great Britain in 2002, with over 1,000 units still in service.

Turners (Soham) Ltd. bought its last Gardner powered ERFs in 1988 and 1989; just before the Gardner option was de-listed by ERF. E576 PEX was new in 1988 and was one of six identical tractive units. They had 6LXDT engines rated at 290 bhp (290T) with Eaton Twin-Splitter 12-speed gearboxes. For the last couple of years in service E576 was used almost daily for taking trailers to the Vehicle Inspectorate Testing Station for annual testing and plating. In summer 2002 the lorry was sold for preservation. (Photo: Author)

Second hand Gardner engines are still in demand, with eight-cylinder units particularly sought after. This was proven at an auction held near Penrith on 3rd November 2001. The transport firm G. A. Stamper was disposing of some of its assets and these included several derelict Atkinsons and Seddon Atkinsons. All had Gardner engines, ranging from 6LX, 6LXB, 8LXB, and 8LXCT. Every one was sold, with those lorries having eight-cylinder engines being sold for between £2,200 and £3,000, well in excess of normal scrap values. One bidder bought most of the lorries, no doubt for their engines, which would almost certainly finish up in Hong Kong or the Middle East. Even these Gardner units lying about the yard sold for good prices.
(Photos: Author)

GARDNER

LEFT: Another place where Gardner engines are still in great demand and are in constant use is the travelling fair. Amusement caterers have relied on Gardner's for two or three generations and they have some of the oldest units still in service. This 6LW was photographed at Newark-on-Trent in May 2002. (Photo: Author)

BELOW: Reproduction of a Gardner brochure from 1981, mentioning the newly introduced turbo-charged engines.

The modern Gardner engine – something very special.

The production of a Gardner engine is not a thing to be hurried — there's too much pride at stake for a thing like that. The modern engine is still produced with the same care, precision and craftsmanship that has established the Gardner reputation.

Even today, each engine is individually built by one man — from the crankshaft upwards.

Similarly, each engine is individually performance tested for several hours —

and just in case it might be thought that this kind of dedication means antiquated methods, take a look at some of the Gardner production areas. High capital investment over the years has established modern foundries, machine shops and assembly shops with equally modern standards to match. Indeed, quality is more easily kept in control at Gardners because of the very high percentage of engine components

which are manufactured on site at Patricroft.

The lightweight engine

Due to the very high aluminium content, the Gardner engine is amongst the lightest in production and until recently all engines have been naturally aspirated. The Gardner research and development team have, however, kept a very watchful eye on the progress of turbo charged engines and they are now available from

Gardners.

The benefits of improved fuel economy, higher power output and quieter running, combined with a substantial reduction in the weight per horsepower, makes the Gardner Turbo a very attractive proposition indeed.

The building of an engine

A feature of the Gardner LX series of engines is a crankcase of aluminium alloy construction, pre-loaded vertically

and transversely. It accommodates the crankshaft, dynamically balanced and manufactured from chromium molybdenum steel with hollow bored crankpins and main journals in eight or ten bearings, dependant on the number of cylinders.

The coolant is circulated by a pump, mechanically driven and not relying on belts, to the base of the cylinders and is transferred to the cylinder head via synthetic rubber joint rings

independent of the main gasket. The patented Gardner dual wax thermostat elements effect automatic temperature control with a built in safeguard against thermostat failure. Pistons are constructed from medium silicon aluminium alloy and have the Gardner innovated hemispherical combustion chambers formed in the piston crown.

Chromium plated rings on these pistons give a long piston ring life.

The Gardner Pattern Shop-the origin of the engine crafted by hand in wood and resin.

Casting in the Aluminium foundry.

All Gardner pistons are cast at the factory.

Sophisticated machinery under the watchful eye of skilled craftsmen ensures Gardner quality standards are maintained.

Reproduction of a page from a 1986 Gardner brochure illustrating the 6LYT engine. Note how the injection pump drive and that for other auxiliary units was taken from the flywheel end of the engine, completely different to any previous Gardner designs.

6LYT

POWER AT 1800 RPM	300 BHP	330 BHP	350 BHP
MAX TORQUE AT 1200 RPM	950 LB FT	1085 LB FT	1140 LB FT
S.F.C.: LB/BHP/HR	0.320	0.320	0.323

DESIGNED FOR 400 BHP AND BEYOND

TRADITIONAL PROVEN GARDNER TECHNOLOGY

ALUMINIUM CRANKCASE

CAST IRON CYLINDER HEADS AND BLOCK

IMPROVED FUEL ECONOMY

LIGHT WEIGHT, COMPACT, EXTERNAL DIMENSIONS

MEETS FUTURE LEGISLATION ON SMOKE EMISSION AND NOISE

After the Hawker Siddeley takeover of Gardner's there was little change to the style of letterheads used, apart from the reference to the new owners at the bottom of the paper.

GARDNER

L. GARDNER & SONS LTD.
ESTABLISHED 1868

BRANCHES

LONDON
130 BRIXTON HILL SW2 1RS
TELEPHONE: 01-671 0978/9
TELEX: 27717

GLASGOW
124 ST. VINCENT STREET, G2 5ER
TELEPHONE: 041-221 0887/8
TELEX: 778513

REGISTERED OFFICE
BARTON HALL ENGINE WORKS,
PATRICROFT, ECCLES, MANCHESTER, M30 7WA.

TELEPHONE: 061-789 2201.   TELEX: 668023
TELEGRAMS: GARDWORKS ECCLES MANCHESTER
SPARES ORDERS & ENQUIRIES - TELEX: 666994 ELGSPS G

DIESEL ENGINES

AUTOMOTIVE   MARINE
RAIL TRACTION   INDUSTRIAL

OUR REF.............................

YOUR REF.............................

REGISTERED IN ENGLAND - NO. 68237   A HAWKER SIDDELEY COMPANY

engines powered an increasing number of lorries from these assemblers. Production could only be increased slowly at Barton Hall, but it was insufficient to cater for a booming market. These rival engines were more powerful than Gardner's 6LXB, and in some specifications even the 8LXB. They were also considerably cheaper.

Another important factor was the lorry driver's opinion, which suddenly counted. In those years there was full employment and a driver could resign from his job on a Friday evening and be virtually guaranteed to commence another one on Monday morning. Many of them did this simply because another firm was running newer, or more powerful lorries and whereas a Gardner engined vehicle was many a driver's ambition at one time, almost overnight this perspective changed. Owners and operators that had traditionally been 'Gardner men' through and through also became weary of waiting at least six months for their favourite engine, so they turned in desperation to other power units or even continental lorries. They were often pleasantly surprised to discover that many were now equal to Gardner's in all respects apart from fuel consumption, but a cheaper purchase price went some way to compensating for this. A Cummins 14 litre unit was 3 hundredweights heavier than a Gardner 6LXB and 15% worse on fuel consumption. But if the driver liked the engine and lorry, then well and good: road haulage was a growth industry, it was profitable then, and driver and owner were equally satisfied.

By the early seventies the clamour was for "more power" from all quarters and maximum weight articulated lorries were expected to have 220–230 bhp as standard. The only Gardner automotive engine able to provide such output was the expensive 8LXB. As the decade progressed expectations changed until 265–290 bhp became normal. Such power ratings were achieved by turbo-charging, and some of these engines from continental makers achieved very high outputs from much smaller swept volumes than the 10.45 litres Gardner '180' six-cylinder unit, let alone the 13.93 litres from eight-cylinders making up the '240'.

Hugh Gardner was vehemently opposed to using turbo-charging as a way of increasing power outputs of Gardner designs. He stated quite categorically that if a turbo-charger entered the works he would quit. This was not an empty threat because back in 1939 some junior Gardner family members had designed and built a small diesel engine that threatened Hugh's LW, 4LK, and L3 units. By then these were the backbone of the company, so Hugh issued an ultimatum that unless he was given complete charge of engine development he would resign. This he actually did and left Barton Hall for two months until his terms were agreed. Needless to say the 'rebel' engine was scrapped.

Most other British automotive diesel engine manufacturers introduced turbo-charged engines to compete with the growing influx of continental and Scandinavian models. Hugh believed the concept over-stressed an engine and it was offensive to his purist engineering principles. In simple terms turbo-charging is a means of forcing an increased volume of air into a cylinder to allow extra fuel necessary for greater power to be burned cleanly. This is achieved by harnessing waste exhaust gases to spin a small turbine, which in turn compresses incoming air. More air in a cylinder on its compression stroke permits cleaner combustion of diesel fuel.

This stance of Hugh Gardner's had been more than justified through the years because Barton Hall could never meet its customers' demands for engines. For decades Gardner's sales team had led comfortable existences, with engines being sold by allocation. As an example, in the year 1949 a total of 3,854 engines of all types left Patricroft. By 1971 this had risen to 6,189 units and the majority of these were six and eight-cylinder types, which took longer to manufacture and assemble. So it can be argued that productivity had increased at Barton Hall over a period of time. Hugh Gardner still maintained his own private engine design office staffed with three resident draughtsmen, but their brief was to put on paper his ideas for improving existing designs, rather than to plan a new range of more powerful engines. It is worth recording that even some dyed-in-the-wool Gardner operators started to experiment with fitting turbo-chargers, but the factory frowned upon such actions and invalidated any possible warranty claims.

By the early seventies British manufacturing industry as a whole was beset by several difficulties including confrontational industrial relations. In particular, communist agitators had infiltrated trades unions in the motor vehicles sector, of which Gardner's was a constituent. Also at this time, monetary inflation was rampant and the Conservative government of the day with Edward Heath (later Sir Edward) as Prime Minister implemented a Prices and Incomes Policy. After Stage One, a complete pay award freeze, Stage Two effectively and legally, limited the amount of wages increase a company could pay. In line with government guidelines, and indeed legislation, Gardner's offered its workforce a rise of one pound plus 5% in response to trade unions demanding a 15% increase. In spring 1973 a lengthy and damaging dispute erupted at Barton Hall works that lasted for fourteen weeks. During this period no engines left the factory to the chagrin of customers.

Notwithstanding the fact that it would have been illegal for the company to offer substantially more than it did, there were other underlying causes to this conflict. Shop floor employees believed their earnings had fallen below the average of skilled workers at other engineering firms in the Manchester area. In August 1972, when a national agreement ended, Gardner's had adjusted basic pay and bonus rates. It was claimed that this action had adversely affected bonuses earned by pieceworkers. This unrest simmered until the following February when the union called for a ban on piece-working with non-pieceworkers refusing to work overtime in support. Consequently engine production was reduced during February and March 1973.

Gardner's management responded by threatening to suspend employees refusing to return to piecework, or taking "irregular industrial action", for two days every week. The first 'lay-off' day was Monday 19th March 1973 and following union advice, the majority of the dayshift reported for work as normal. The trades unions requested a meeting with management but this was refused until all shop floor personnel involved were working on piecework again. A mass meeting ensued and a decision made to withdraw labour completely with official union support. The company immediately suspended 300 pieceworkers and 1,700 other employees were put on a three-day

The prolonged and damaging strike of 1973 caused many skilled employees to leave Gardner's and find employment elsewhere. When production resumed some rationalisation was inevitable and the trend-setting LW series of engines was discontinued in 1974. After being available continuously for 43 years the last LW engines were assembled in May 1974 and must have been the longest running, engine range available in Great Britain. These 3LWs were the last of that cylinder configuration, dispatched in March 1974.

week. The dispute escalated rapidly to challenge national Prices and Incomes Policy and soon the entire works was at a virtual standstill with some 2,000 employees on strike.

And so had begun the worst industrial relations dispute in Gardner's history. It was protracted and bitter. To prevent completed engines leaving Patricroft, strikers occupied the packing and dispatch departments. They formed a continuous picket and measures had to be taken to deny them access to the remainder of the site. Fortunately the spare parts section was located away from the main premises and was not affected, allowing normal service to operators.

Despite overtures to management by respected local Labour M.P. Stan Orme, and Tony Benn, then Labour M.P. for a Bristol constituency where Gardner engined buses were assembled, Gardner's refused to talk until the strikers returned to work. Gordon Thompstone, Gardner's Works Director was a qualified solicitor and experienced mediator. He headed the company's negotiating team. In 1973 he was also serving as President of the local engineering employer's federation. It is firmly believed that Gardner's was targeted by unions led by communists because of Gordon Thompstone's prominence in employer and union discussions on a wider scale. After

fourteen weeks of acrimony and hardship for many strikers' families the strike collapsed. No concessions were made by the company and despite the unions claiming a great victory the workers returned on the same terms as before.

Until 1973 Gardner's had enjoyed reasonably good industrial relations with employees and unions. There had been a couple of previous difficulties, firstly in 1947 when the apprentices went on strike as part of a dispute that affected other Manchester firms. A more serious withdrawal of labour had taken place in the centenary year, 1968. Before the annual July holiday shutdown that year the Directors

J.H.S. (Hugh) Gardner photographed at his home, Barton House, Worsley. He retired in 1978 at the age of 74 after more than 50 years service with the company. His knowledge of diesel engines was unsurpassed and he was closely involved in the development of the pioneering Gardner L2 and LW designs in the late 1920s. With his brother John he introduced the 6LX and its derivatives that kept Gardner's at the forefront of automotive engine applications for so many years.

announced that there would be a bonus payment of one weeks wages to everybody on the books on 31st August. In early August a certain shop steward in the iron foundry started casting the Gardner name upside down on the largest iron casting, the 8L3B crankcase, for some reason only known to him. Despite formal warnings this continued until finally he was suspended. The other foundry shop stewards took up the matter and called a strike in the entire foundry complex. This was not supported by the remainder of the works who wished to continue making engines. An ultimatum was issued to the strikers for them to return to work or consider themselves dismissed. Eventually they trooped back in early September, but they forfeited their centenary bonus. The man who caused the strike left Gardner's shortly afterwards, no doubt hounded out by his former colleagues.

One consequence of the foundry strike was that it eventually led to productivity improvements. To maintain output from the rest of Barton Hall, volunteers were called for to work in the foundry. A motley

crew of various workers, staff, managers, and even a couple of Directors answered the summons and manned the furnaces for about four weeks. It is remembered as a great experience that highlighted several inadequacies. As an example, there was a very complex sand core in a cylinder head casting for the water-cooling jacket for which a worker was allowed forty minutes to make one. A new technique was developed that reduced this time to just 12 seconds!

The 1973 dispute was typical of many in the car and commercial vehicle industry at the time and the cumulative effect of all this industrial action and unrest was to hasten the decline of the manufacturing base of the nation. For Gardner's the strike could not have happened at worse time, struggling as they were to satisfy chassis builders. Engine orders for lorries were insatiable in spite of competition from more powerful, and cheaper, proprietary makes. These were used to fill the continuously expanding market for heavy vehicles.

By the end of 1973 as a result of the strike, production levels had more than halved to 2,937 engines compared with two years before. Moreover, the problems caused by this lengthy and disastrous dispute caused more than 600 employees to leave Barton Hall and find work elsewhere. So, when a settlement was made decisions were taken to rationalize the product catalogue. The revolutionary, trend setting LW range that had been in production for over forty years was discontinued, as was the marine reversing gear. This was replaced by the American designed Twin-Disc type.

However, before the Twin-Disc reversing gear was supplied in unit construction with a Gardner marine engine, there was a period when engine and gearbox had to be obtained separately by the boat builder. In part this was due to Hugh Gardner and his excellent memory. He remembered a time from before the Second World War when Gardner's sold rail traction engines assembled with a well-known make of British gearbox. These transmissions were unreliable and as Gardner's had supplied them they were held to be responsible and had to rectify faults. Bearing this in mind almost 35 years later, Hugh refused point-blank to supply any other manufacturers' marine gearbox with his engines. An outcome of this policy was a serious reduction in marine engine orders, but Hugh was not particularly worried because it released production capacity for extra automotive units. Eventually John Gardner remonstrated with his brother and common sense prevailed. Gardner's started to order Twin-Disc gearboxes directly from the maker and attached them to marine engines at Barton Hall. Boat builders were apparently quite patient customers; they often had to wait up to 2 years for engines after placing an order with 10% deposit.

Throughout the 1970s much of Britain's heavy manufacturing industry was in a chaotic state. Typical of this was the hitherto unthinkable bankruptcy of Rolls Royce Ltd. in 1974. Yet this event opened up an intriguing possibility and opportunity for Gardner's. The Rolls Royce diesel engine factory at Shrewsbury was modern and well equipped, making a range of engines that competed in some of the same markets as Gardner's. By comparison some machinery at Barton Hall was antiquated. In early years Gardner's designed and made most of their manufacturing plant. It was certainly made well; in true Gardner tradition, but by the mid-seventies some machines were over fifty years old. Some departments had been modernised, but other machine shops at Barton Hall still required significant amounts of capital expenditure to bring them up to date. For example, the

crankshaft shop was only equipped with its first grinding tools in 1971. Before then every crankshaft pin and journal was turned on machines designed and made by Gardner's. And some of this equipment dated back to the First World War! When the news about Rolls Royce became known Paul Gardner convened an emergency Board meeting to examine the possibilities offered by the Shrewsbury diesel engine plant. But in the end a decision was made not to open negotiations with the Rolls Royce receiver, because Hugh Gardner stated that if it went ahead he would leave. Paul was asked to apologise for wasting the Board's time.

After the traumas experienced earlier in the decade, by 1975 it was probable that the ageing Gardner Board members were becoming weary and disillusioned about certain aspects of the business. Hugh and John had been used to having total control of the works for so long and they were finding it increasingly frustrating to be challenged by the unions at every instance.

Gradually they were beginning to realise that changes were inevitable and maybe even desirable.

By the year 1975 Hugh Gardner realised the company needed to strengthen its management and Clayton Flint was invited to join the Board. Clayton Flint was not an engineer, but a Senior Partner with a firm of Solicitors that was retained by Gardner's. He was in effect a very experienced "company doctor" and was appointed Independent Chairman, so becoming the first Chairman who was not a member of the family. Gardner's was still a profitable concern but large sums of capital investment were needed to modernise the works. In total £8

million was needed, which was a large amount of money then. The machine shops were in dire need of new equipment and the rudimentary computer system required updating. Virtually every component in a Gardner engine was still manufactured at Barton Hall and whilst this policy ensured the highest quality standards it did increase unit costs considerably. A few short cuts were taken with engine production and output did gradually increase from 120 to 150 engines per week.

This increased productivity was in the main due to upgrading Gardner's foundry. Under the provisions of The Industry Act 1972, financial assistance was available for modernisation schemes and a grant was applied for in February 1976. Gardner cylinder heads and blocks were cast in the traditional manner with green sand moulds produced on jolting machines, with hand ramming and finishing. By changing to a 'cold box' process a high degree of mechanisation was introduced along with improvements in quality. Complementing this change was the replacement of existing foundry cupolas by electric melting of iron. Again, this had several metallurgical advantages and saved manpower. After Gardner's had revamped their foundry, not only was engine output increased, but substantial cost savings were also made. Another benefit was a better working environment for employees.

Under Clayton Flint's more open-minded direction many changes were implemented. One of his first decisions was to ask the three elderly Directors, – 'the trinity', – to consider retirement. Frank Wilkinson stepped down in September 1975, (along with Gordon Thompstone), and Hugh

The thorny problem of certified power outputs from Gardner engines to comply with the legal minimum requirement of 6 bhp per ton from 1972 is discussed fully in Chapter 10. All Gardner engines offered for automotive applications were certified to BSAU 141a:1971 specification and 6LXB and 8LXB units are shown on the test bed on 5th June and 7th July 1972 respectively.

Gardner was persuaded to hand over the reins to the other Directors and retired as Chairman on 1st July 1975. It was suggested to him that instead of running the factory he should concentrate on increasing the power of the 6LXB engine. With this brief Hugh was confined to his research department and took no interest in day-to-day running of the works. John Gardner did remain as Managing Director and for the first time other Directors were able to run their own departments without referring to a higher authority. Paul Gardner took on engine design and at long last, turbo-charging development commenced. Even so, this was done without Hugh Gardner's approval, although no doubt he was aware of it. A testing unit was set up in part of the Cambell Road spares department under Paul's supervision. Dion Houghton retained control of sales, Jim Smith was appointed Works Director, W.R.W. Maddox became Finance Director and Company Secretary, (although he was replaced shortly afterwards by Peter Connor), and Geoff Howarth was Personnel Director.

Even with turbo-charging research in progress based on

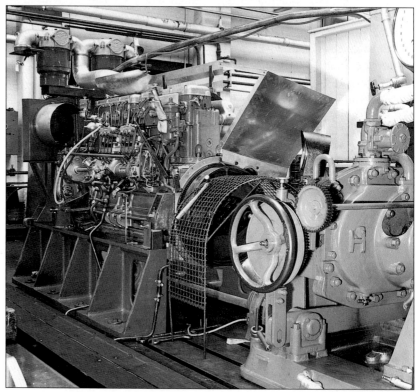

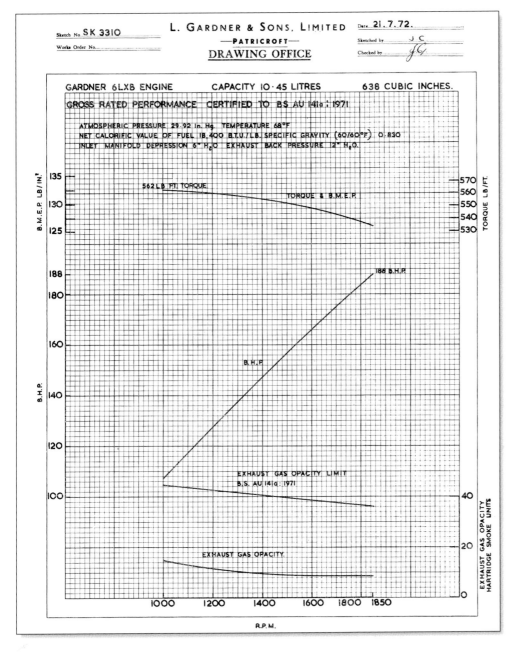

Sketch No. **SK 3310**

Works Order No.

L. GARDNER & SONS, LIMITED
—PATRICROFT—
DRAWING OFFICE

Date **21.7.72.**

Sketched by **J C**

Checked by

GARDNER 6LXB ENGINE   CAPACITY 10·45 LITRES   638 CUBIC INCHES.

GROSS RATED PERFORMANCE CERTIFIED TO BS AU 141a : 1971

ATMOSPHERIC PRESSURE 29.92 In. Hg. TEMPERATURE 68°F
NET CALORIFIC VALUE OF FUEL 18,400 B.T.U./LB. SPECIFIC GRAVITY (60/60°F) 0.830
INLET MANIFOLD DEPRESSION 6" H₂O EXHAUST BACK PRESSURE 12" H₂O.

562 LB FT TORQUE

TORQUE & B.M.E.P.

188 B.H.P.

B.H.P.

EXHAUST GAS OPACITY LIMIT
B.S. AU 141a : 1971

EXHAUST GAS OPACITY.

B.M.E.P. LB/IN.²

B.H.P.

TORQUE LB/FT.

EXHAUST GAS OPACITY HARTRIDGE SMOKE UNITS

R.P.M.

Certificate for a Gardner 6LXB engine for compliance with BSAU 141a:1971 standards and a power output of 188 bhp at 1,850 rpm. It enabled these engines to still be fitted into 30 tons gross weight eight-wheelers, legal on the roads from 1972. The actual tests comprised 100 hours running, with 50 individual cycles of two hours duration.

existing engines it was apparent to John and Paul Gardner that this could only be a stopgap measure and that a totally new design was needed. Paul and his father assembled a new project team that comprised experienced engineers from other companies such as Ruston, and Leyland. Eventually they would create the Gardner 6LY series.

It is now clear that Clayton Flint was brought in to prepare L. Gardner & Sons Ltd. for being taken over. Capital for investing in new machinery was proving difficult to raise. Rumours that Gardner's was up for grabs started to circulate and ironically, a government owned and re-financed Rolls Royce took an interest. Unknown to Gardner's

Directors it had acquired 5% of the shares through nominees and soon bought a further 6%. With a total of 11% of the stock, Rolls Royce had to disclose its interest under Stock Exchange rules. Several other companies including Hanson, and The Laird Group, (Cammell Laird), also made approaches. However, the Board favoured Hawker Siddeley

A Gardner 8LXB marine engine undergoing an inclination test at Patricroft. Obviously in rough seas engines must continue to operate reliably even when not remaining in a vertical plane. To protect bearings from possible oil starvation scavenging type oil pumps were used.

because they were engine makers in marine and industrial markets with no automotive connections. A takeover of Gardner's by Hawker Siddeley was viewed as an ideal 'marriage'.

And on 26th July 1977 a takeover offer by Hawker Siddeley was made for Gardner's. The merchant bank S.G. Warburg & Co. Ltd. made a bid on behalf of Hawker Siddeley Group Limited to acquire the entire L. Gardner & Sons Ltd. ordinary stock units of 25p each in the capital of the company on the basis of 340p in cash. Or, upon election within a specified period, two ordinary shares of 25p each in Hawker Siddeley Group Limited, for each Gardner ordinary stock unit. This offer was declared un-conditional on 16th August 1977 with acceptance having exceeded 90% of the ordinary stock units. Those remaining shareholders who did not accept the offer terms had their stock units compulsorily acquired under the provisions of Section 209 of the Companies Act 1948. Accordingly at 31st December 1977 L. Gardner & Sons Ltd. became a wholly owned subsidiary of Hawker Siddeley Group Limited. And so, appropriately at the close of one year, after 109 years of independence and family control Gardner's became a division of another famous company.

Hawker Siddeley brought a completely different management style and philosophy to Barton Hall. The main consideration was profit; perhaps it was the only factor. A new Managing Director was appointed and Clayton Flint resigned on 31st December 1978, his task completed. There was a feeling among many of Gardner's "old school" that their new masters valued academic qualifications much more than years of experience of making engines. Several long-serving and valued managers volunteered for early retirement. No doubt much of this was a 'new broom' syndrome and is common after a takeover. It is remembered that under Hugh Gardner a Director might receive all of two memos in twenty years, but under Hawker Siddeley they averaged two per day! These notes were deemed necessary to ensure the recipient was fully aware of the company's intentions, and indicated

the best way of achieving its aims. For the first time strict budgetary controls were given to each department and monthly meetings took place under Hawker Siddeley's supervision to discover any weaknesses in management. Pricing policy was reviewed and spare parts prices were raised substantially to generate more income. A review of automotive engine selling prices compared with manufacturing costs revealed that most were being sold to chassis makers at very slim profit margins, and some installers were even buying them at below cost price. Consequently ex-works prices were raised by amounts varying between 7.7% and 14.8%, depending on which customer it was. For example, a Gardner 6LXB for ERF was increased from £3,323 to £3,579, and a 6HLXB for a Bristol passenger chassis became £3,782 instead of £3,444. Because automotive engines destined for the

The following notes are reproduced verbatim from a document (from Hawker Siddeley) prepared in July 1976 outlining considerations about an Hawker Siddeley / Gardner alliance.

1. Gardner has gross assets of £13.75m according to its Balance Sheet at 31.12.76.

2. Gardner designs and manufactures diesel engines in the range 188-260 bhp, mainly for automotive purposes. Subsidiaries of Hawker Siddeley produce a wide range of diesels from the smallest up to 11,000 bhp, but very few are in the Gardner power range, and none are for automotive purposes. The merger will not, therefore, lead to the creation of a one-third market share in this range of product.

3. Information on Gardner and Hawker Siddeley is contained in their respective Annual Reports and Accounts for 1976. Further information on the activities of Hawker Siddeley is contained in the brochure "What we manufacture and where". Gardner's factory is at Eccles, Manchester, where they employ some 2,275 people.

4. Gardner's direct exports were some 20% of its total sales in 1976; these sales were made through agents – it has no overseas selling or manufacturing establishments of its own, nor any licensing arrangements with foreign companies. Hawker Siddeley exports between 60% and 75% of its various ranges of diesels, partly through agencies and partly through its own selling companies. Some engines (in the smaller ranges) are manufactured or assembled abroad, by wholly or partly owned companies (mainly in areas where legal restrictions or tariffs preclude the import of complete engines). Petter has licensed the technology for part of its range to the Onan Corporation of U.S.A. (in which Hawker Siddeley has a 37% interest).

5. The automotive diesel industry consists partly of motor companies who make engines for their own vehicles, as well as other applications; Ford (who also make tractors), Leyland, Bedford. Partly of companies who make diesels for their tractors and agricultural machinery (Perkins a subsidiary of Massey Ferguson), David Brown, and International Harvester, and three independent manufacturers (Cummins, Gardner, and Rolls). In terms of numbers, Perkins and Ford produce over 200,000 units a year, and Leyland about half that number, followed by Bedford with about 50,000. The majority of their engines are smaller than those produced by Gardner, whose main competitors are Cummins (American owned) and Rolls. Cummins is much the larger, with about 30,000 engines (about half of which go to the automotive market and half for industrial and marine use), many of which are exported in accordance with the requirements of their world-wide business (e.g. the U.K. is the sole source for their small V-engines). Gardner produce about 4,500 engines and Rolls somewhat fewer. The majority of Rolls engines are used for generating sets, marine propulsion, small locomotives, and for tanks and other military applications.

6. The engines go mainly to the manufacturers of heavy goods vehicles, heavy construction equipment and buses – Ford, Leyland, Foden, ERF, Seddon Atkinson. But it the ultimate customer who usually picks the engine he wants, and the vehicle manufacturer normally offers his customer a choice.

7. There is little foreign competition inside the U.K. from imported automotive diesel engines, but there is of course, substantial competition for the commercial vehicle industry from imported vehicles – firms like Volvo, Scania and Mercedes.

8. Hawker Siddeley's object is to use its financial resources (as well as its long experience in the production and world-wide sales and servicing of diesel engines) to assist and encourage the growth of Gardner's long established business of supplying specialised diesel engines for those applications where fuel economy and reliability is of paramount importance. Whilst it may ultimately be necessary to find additional capacity elsewhere (due to constraints of the present site), the business would continue to be carried out on the present site quite independently of Hawker Siddeley's other diesel activities – in Hawker Siddeley's view it would be wrong to attempt any consolidation of production because of the extent to which the qualities of the Gardner engine are attributable to the manufacturing methods used. There will therefore be no change in employment as a result of the merger. Hawker Siddeley expect to make substantial capital investment in Gardner over the next few years.

9. Historically, Gardner's have always been able to sell all the engines they can make (and have been criticised for failing to satisfy all demands during periods of high economic activity). It cannot be certain that this will continue indefinitely, in that the smaller vehicle manufacturers might lose their independence, and the larger ones increase their efforts to persuade customers to accept their own engines (e.g. Leyland and the B15 "Titan" bus). In addition, British vehicle builders may find their market diminished by imported competition. Should this situation ever come to pass, Hawker Siddeley's worldwide marketing organisation on the generating set and marine side would enable alternative outlets to be obtained.

10. As an example of previous acquisitions by Hawker Siddeley, when R.A. Lister & Co. Ltd. was acquired in 1965, its sales were £16m. In 1976 they were £62m. The number of cylinder lines produced has almost doubled, and a substantial further expansion scheme is now in progress.

TOP RIGHT: By the mid-1970s the once mighty British Leyland Group was in terminal decline. Although it was still a massive organisation, failures of under-developed new engine designs meant it had to turn to Gardner's for engines for its B20 Titan double deck bus. Here a Gardner 6LXB to Leyland B20 specification is undergoing testing of a Plessey hydraulic pump arrangement.

BELOW: A tranquil scene in Hong Kong harbour with Chinese junks plying their trade. It has long been every junk owner's ambition to have a Gardner engine, and over the years thousands of second hand engines have been exported there from Great Britain. Even in the early years of this century, with no new traditional Gardner engines having been made for a decade, demand is still strong, although sources are now becoming scarce. (Photo: Ming Yuen Studio)

The Board of Directors of L. Gardner & Sons Limited in July 1977 when the takeover offer from Hawker Siddeley was made. Back row left to right, Tom Screwbrie, Geoff Howarth, Dion Houghton, Jim Smith. Front row left to right, John Gardner, Clayton Flint (Chairman), Paul Gardner.

home market represented some 85% of total output it was imperative that they were sold at a profit.

Hawker Siddeley's takeover even caused Hugh Gardner to ponder about retirement. After all, he was 73 years of age, but before he finally relinquished all influence at Barton Hall there was one more development to come. His policy of extracting maximum fuel efficiency in relation to power output was maintained with the final versions of his LXB engines. In 1978 the six-cylinder unit was re-designated 6LXC and it produced 201 bhp at 1,920 rpm. Correspondingly, the 8LXC gave 265 bhp also at 1,920 rpm. This engine now boasted the lowest specific weight to power ratio in Gardner's history. The extra power made the 8LXC more competitive in articulated lorries,

and the 6LXC remained very popular with rigid eight-wheeler operators. Some measure of the attention to detail paid to design by Gardner's over the years can be gauged by the statistic that the 6LXC engine consumed just 0.324 lbs. of fuel per hp/hour compared with the 0.41 lbs. of fuel per hp/hour obtained from the pioneering Gardner direct injection 6L2 engine of 1930. Remember, this unit then set standards of fuel consumption unmatched by other manufacturers for many years. These LXC engines were Hugh Gardner's swansong and were the last naturally aspirated Gardner automotive engines to be announced.

Hugh Gardner finally retired in 1978 aged 74. For over half a century he was involved in diesel

engine design and development and was one of the pioneering engineers who brought the Gardner name to the forefront. His family's firm was his life and he was fiercely protective of the standards associated with Gardner's reputation. In his years as Managing Director he could be autocratic in running Barton Hall and his Board meetings were legendary. No more than two per year were held, mainly to approve his decisions. Similarly, annual general meetings of shareholders were brief affairs, the official business taking fifteen minutes and the hospitality two hours! But over the years profitability was maintained, sales were at the maximum the works could cope with, and there was very little that could be criticised from a shareholder's viewpoint. Like all people Hugh Gardner had his shortcomings and away from the office he is fondly remembered as a wonderfully caring family man who was generous and excellent company. He had designed and produced one of the outstanding diesel engines of the twentieth century, viz the Gardner 6LX '150' and its derivatives. Hugh Gardner should be remembered for that alone.

10

NEW ENGINE DESIGNS

There was plenty of attention paid by the new owners to Gardner's financial policies during their first year of dominion. Cost controls were effective and benefits from modernisation schemes, such as that instigated under Clayton Flint for the foundry, were coming to fruition. This was reflected in the company's accounts, although price increases referred to in the previous chapter did not come into effect until later in 1978. But because demand for Gardner's products remained healthy, the figures for 1978 revealed that turnover had increased from £23,654,000 in the preceding year to £29,256,000. Comparable trading profits were £2,582,000 in 1977 (10.9%) and £3,646,000 (12.5%) for 1978.

One historical point of contention between Gardner's and its automotive customers was the policy of what was perceived as excessive pricing mark-up of a chassis powered by a Gardner engine. By the late seventies, several years of high inflation had caused costs of lorries to double at least, compared with ten years before. Gardner's always believed that the chassis makers exploited the high

esteem operators had for their engines. This is illustrated by the following information compiled in February 1978.

ENGINE PRICE (ex-Works)

1. A 6LXB '188' engine is £234 more to a chassis manufacturer than a Rolls 220. This is 11.5% more than a Rolls for 30 bhp less.
2. A 6LXB '188' is the same price as a Cummins 250 for 62 bhp less.
3. An 8LXB '250' is £840 more to a chassis manufacturer than a Cummins 250, i.e. 34% more (for the same power).
4. An 8LXB '250' is £640 more to a chassis manufacturer than a Rolls 265, i.e. 24% more for 15 bhp less.

FUEL SAVINGS (At 1978 Fuel Prices)

- A 6LXB will show approximately 8.00 mpg (in a 32 tons gross weight artic.)
  A Rolls 220 will show approximately 7.00 mpg (in a similar lorry)
  On 80,000 miles per annum saving is £957 (by the Gardner engine)

- An 8LXB will show approximately 7.5 mpg (in a 32 tons gross weight artic.)
  A Cummins 250 will show approximately 7.00 mpg (in a similar lorry)
  On 80,000 miles per annum the saving is £510 (by the Gardner engine)

MARK-UPS (Using ERF As The Example)

ERF pay £840 extra for an 8LXB Assuming they add 30% handling,
£840 + £253 = £1,093
Add 25% to allow
a dealer discount of 20% = £ 274
TOTAL £1,367

The mark-up therefore should be £1,367
In fact, ERF charge £3,000 more for a tractive unit powered by a Gardner 8LXB '250'.

In defence of ERF, its salesmen would reason that an operator could recoup the extra purchase cost in fuel saved over about six years with a lorry covering average general haulage mileage annually. Even back in the late seventies a premium goods vehicle like an ERF had an expected operational life of at least eight years. Moreover, residual value for a Gardner powered lorry was usually better than that of a Cummins or Rolls powered example, and the owner would receive more for it when it was sold.

Another argument to support a salesman's case for supplying a Gardner engine was the results of a 1979 survey of 9,488 heavy lorries fitted with sixteen different types of engines. This comprehensive review was of engine maintenance costs for lorries operating at 30/32 tons gross weight and all had covered a minimum of 200,000 miles in service, after being supplied new earlier in the seventies.

Gardner's pre-eminent position in this prestigious report came as no surprise to loyal operators. They had known for years that these engines were the most cost-effective.

Towards the close of the seventies decade there was still tremendous optimism in the commercial vehicles industry and the chassis builders were exceedingly bullish about their prospects for 1979. Estimated engine requirements from Barton Hall exceeded production capacity of 150 per week, and it is interesting to reproduce this data (right).

This was equivalent to 189 six-cylinder engines weekly and Gardner's would have been unable to meet this demand by a considerable margin if the estimates had not proved to be very optimistic. For instance, Seddon never remotely produced 41 passenger chassis monthly for a sustained period, and others in this same market such as Leyland Group companies Daimler and Bristol, overestimated their sales. Interestingly, because of development failures by new Leyland designs, that company had turned to Gardner engines for buses it

ENGINE MAINTENANCE COSTS COMPARISON

Details of repairs cost per 100,000 miles, excluding routine servicing and maintenance.

POSITION	ENGINE MAKE & TYPE	COST, PENCE PER MILE
1	GARDNER 6LXB	0.265
2	GARDNER 8LXB	0.334
3	CUMMINS 250	0.394
4	AEC AV760	0.452
5	MERCEDES OM335	0.743
6	CUMMINS 220	0.765
7	VOLVO TD100	0.853
8	DAF DU825	0.893
9	M.A.N. 232	0.898
10	SCANIA DS11	0.943
11	ROLLS ROYCE 220	0.951
12	MAGIRUS 413L V8	1.392
13	VOLVO TD70	1.469
14	LEYLAND O.680	1.494
15	LEYLAND 510	1.591
16	SCANIA DS8	1.626

SOURCE: *"TRANSPORT ENGINEER"*– Journal of The I.R.T.E.

CUSTOMER	6 CYL. UNITS / MONTH	8 CYL. UNITS / MONTH
Seddon Atkinson	70	42
Seddon (PSV)	41	
Leyland Group	175	
ERF	100	70
Foden	84	16
M.C.W.	45	
Dennis	12	
Dennison	3	1
Pelican	3	1
G.E.S.A.	6	
Miscellaneous	7	3
6LXB Marine	8	
8LXB Marine		8
8L3B		8
TOTAL	554	149

supplied to London Transport. Traditionally, for almost 60 years, AEC and Leyland powered vehicles had provided most of London's public transport.

Included among Hawker Siddeley's portfolio of engine making companies were Petter, Lister Diesels, and Mirlees Blackstone. Their ranges covered the smallest of industrial types to massive marine main engines. Many of the bigger units were turbo-charged, but because none was for automotive applications this particular technology could not be applied at Barton Hall. At first Paul Gardner and his team used the 6LXB engine as the basis of their turbo-charging project. When his uncle, Hugh, finally produced the 6LXC version, Paul turned his attention to that and in July 1979 he had the first official turbo-charged Gardner engine on test. It was designated 6LXCT and when this type entered production in June 1981 it was rated, in standard form, for 230 bhp at 1,900 rpm. Maximum torque was 673 lbs.ft at 1,400 rpm. A proprietary Holset turbo-charger was used and the 6LXCT maintained Gardner's reputation for fuel frugality. In the first year of availability a total of 175 of the new engines entered service in lorries built by ERF, Foden, Scammell, and Seddon Atkinson. Passenger vehicles assembled by Leyland, Dennis, and MCW also fitted vertical 6LXCTs while a horizontal version (6HLXCT) was also used by Dennis and Leyland for coach chassis. Gardner's tradition of offering an eight-cylinder automotive engine was perpetuated when their turbo-charged 8LXCT was announced. It produced 300 bhp at 1,900 rpm and a whopping 880 lbs.ft of torque at 1,400 rpm.

ENGINE	TEST BED OUTPUT	BSAU 141a OUTPUT
6LX	150 bhp @ 1,700 rpm	157 bhp @ 1,700 rpm
6LXB	180 bhp @ 1,850 rpm	188 bhp @ 1,850 rpm
6LXC	193 bhp @ 1,920 rpm	201 bhp @ 1,920 rpm
6LXCT	220 bhp @ 1,900 rpm	230 bhp @ 1,900 rpm
8LXB	240 bhp @ 1,850 rpm	250 bhp @ 1,850 rpm
8LXC	255 bhp @ 1,920 rpm	265 bhp @ 1,920 rpm
8LXCT	290 bhp @ 1,900 rpm	300 bhp @ 1,900 rpm

The table above outlines the development of what can best be described as traditional Gardner engines, although they eventually incorporated turbo-charging. Their design ancestry dated back to Hugh Gardner's immortal 6LX '150' of 1958.

The significance of these power ratings is that Gardner's could always be confident of accuracy because they were established on a test bed. Remember, every Gardner engine was tested and run for several hours before it left the works and any necessary adjustments made. British Standards BSAU 141a allowed a 5% tolerance for manufacturers whose engine outputs were determined by the fuel pump that had originally been calibrated on an injection fuel pump tester. This permitted Gardner's to claim part of that allowance. It was important for compliance with the minimum 6 bhp per ton legislation and it ensured the 6LXB could legally be fitted in rigid eight wheelers at 30 tons gross vehicle weight after 1972. Similarly, when the Gardner 6LXC became available it could be used for 32 tons gross vehicle weight articulated tractive units. (The relevant bhp is that at the flywheel, i.e. nett. Thus 188 bhp less that power absorbed driving auxiliaries such as fan, water pump, compressor, fuel pump, = 180 bhp nett).

To clarify the thorny problem of quoted brake horsepower ratings the author has quoted verbatim paragraphs from a letter written to him by Paul Gardner in April 2002.

"Because, almost from the 1960s, Gardner engines were always struggling for power, and whilst this didn't matter too much when there were full order books, it certainly did when the power/weight ratio of 6 bhp/ton was first introduced. You make the point quite clearly because the 30 ton rigid vehicle and 32 ton tractor unit suddenly became outside the Gardner power range. The point is that it was the installed power that mattered and the 6LXB nett at the flywheel, after auxiliary powers were removed was about 174 bhp. At 6 bhp/ton this only allowed 29 tons, which was a loss of 1 ton of payload which would not have been popular. To overcome this situation, and I regret it was me that initiated this, knowing the power we claimed was set on the test bed, we could claim up to 5% allowance. This on the 6LXB would have given 189 bhp, but we claimed 188 bhp, which less the 6 bhp required for the auxiliaries gave 182 bhp and thus the 6LXB continued to be acceptable for the 30 ton rigid vehicle. The 6LXC was a later engine making use of the tolerance. It developed 192 bhp on the test bed and claiming 5 per cent on this would give 201.6 bhp. We claimed 201 bhp which less the power

of the auxiliaries gave 193 bhp and therefore the engine was acceptable in the 32 ton tractor unit. This was not really a satisfactory situation. In a way I felt we were cheating (legally), but it did keep us in the two most important sectors of the truck market. The proper solution was to have had an engine on top of the job and not using the expense and length of 8 cylinders, although this is a beautifully smooth unit and looks and sounds superb when we test them today. Of course you know the story associated with this, but I do feel that this was a turning point in Gardner's history.

You may wonder why I have written on this subject at length. It is simply to illustrate that the 2 power ratings quoted and relative torques can get you into all sorts of trouble, which is why we have altered some of your figures in the charts."

(Author's note: the charts referred to appear in Appendix C. Paul Gardner amended my original drafts with works data, and it is now reproduced in Appendix C).

There were echoes of the 1973 strike when in October 1980 another industrial dispute erupted at Barton Hall. Hawker Siddeley announced plans to reduce the workforce at Gardner's by 600 employees and the trade unions objected. Once again a 'sit-in' ensued and the entire site, including the spares department and offices, were occupied. It was a serious situation and no members of staff or management were allowed access to the works.

In the year 1983 the British gross vehicle weight for an articulated lorry was raised to 38 tonnes (37.4 imperial tons) on five axles. The legal requirement of minimum 6 bhp per ton was rapidly becoming outmoded as operators decided

what power was necessary for higher weights. At first 290 bhp was declared the comfortable minimum, but soon attitudes changed and 320, and then 340 bhp was deemed desirable. Once again Gardner's found themselves at a disadvantage in the horsepower stakes with only their 8LXCT offering just the perceived minimum output for a maximum weight artic. New lorries were becoming more sophisticated and expensive and road transport profit margins were getting smaller, so there was a growing reluctance by many operators to specify the expensive Gardner option.

During this period there were many outside factors affecting Gardner's. The economy was in serious recession and sales of new commercial vehicles were badly affected The company was losing some of its established customer base and Leyland Group subsidiaries that used Gardner engines, namely Guy, Daimler, and Bristol, were closed. Notwithstanding the effects of the economic downturn, sales of ERF, Foden, and Seddon Atkinson lorries were in decline and ERF production halved. Foden was experiencing financial problems and would lose its independence, and Seddon Atkinson was suffering because of uncertainty about its future. All three companies easily comprised Gardner's largest market and were under severe competition from imported makes.

Concurrent with the recession were the stringent economic and severe social policies pursued by a Conservative government led by Margaret Thatcher (later Baroness Thatcher). "Thatcherism" encouraged keen (some would claim ruthless) competitiveness between companies and only the efficient ones prospered.

In March 1984 Gardner's announced the first new engine design from the team established almost six years earlier. Whilst this unit had several new features it incorporated components from the Gardner 6LXCT, and its precursors. This long-awaited new Gardner engine was designated 6LXDT and had a swept volume of 12.7 litres. Its cylinder dimensions were 5.125 inches bore and 6.25 inches stroke. The engine was turbo-charged from the outset and its standard power rating was 270 bhp at 1,900 rpm. An optional output of 250 bhp was also available, and later, from 1987, more powerful versions could be specified.

The 6LXDT was the first Gardner design to have a proprietary fuel injection pump in its entirety and the CAV Majormec unit was used. This allowed higher pressures and a faster rate of injection than Gardner's own pump. Centrally located CAV fuel injectors were also fitted. This engine also differed from established Gardner practice in that the triplex timing chain only drove the camshaft and injection pump. A separate duplex chain was used for the alternator, and power steering pump. This arrangement enabled more power to be transmitted and provided faster rotational speeds. Stronger, double, exhaust valve springs were also used to facilitate exhaust braking, again for the first time on a Gardner engine. However, because the valve train was already at its maximum capability this idea was not very successful and, in fact, most operators removed the extra valve spring to provide durability.

Relative to its power, the 6LXDT maintained Gardner's reputation for good economy and a specific minimum fuel consumption of

0.315lb/bhp/hr was claimed. Other attributes of this engine were larger valves and bearing surfaces and the oil cooler pump was crankcase mounted. Overall external dimensions and weight of the 6LXDT were comparable with the 6LXCT, which remained in production for the time being.

Another Gardner custom was revived after an absence of eleven years and an interesting potential addition to the sales catalogue in 1984 was a five-cylinder turbo-charged automotive engine. This was the 5LXCT of 8.7 litres displacement, and was specifically aimed at the urban, rear-engined passenger vehicles market, where it would be shorter and cheaper than a conventional six-cylinder unit. During development it was set to produce 185 bhp at 1,900 with 560 lbs.ft of torque at 1,300 rpm. A slightly less powerful version, 170 bhp at 1,850 rpm was also planned. The 5LXCT shared all internal components with the 6LXCT, but its CAV fuel injection system was based on that of the 6LXDT. Only six engines were built for 'seeding' purposes. Leyland installed two, one for Northern General, and the other into an Alexander Northern chassis. Dennis also took two engines that saw service in Leicester. MCW had one 5LXCT but because they were experiencing difficulties and were soon to close, it was never used. Interestingly ERF were allocated one engine but never took delivery of it. Whilst the engines performed well in service this five-cylinder design never entered production.

In autumn 1984 the first entirely new Gardner engine design in almost thirty years was announced. Described as "brand new from the sump plug upward" this was the massive 15.5 litres capacity 6LYT. It

had been six years in planning and development but adhered to time-honoured Gardner principles of minimum weight in relation to size. Another long-standing trait retained was a separate aluminium alloy crankcase and detachable cast iron cylinder block. By then virtually every other engine manufacturer had long since standardised on monobloc cast iron crankcases and cylinder blocks.

New ground was broken with many aspects of the Gardner 6LYT. It was designed as a 'metric' engine for producing at least 400 bhp. The cylinder bore dimension was 140 mm (5.51 inches) and the stroke was 168 mm (6.61 inches). Standard power rating was 320 bhp at 1,800 rpm with 1,030 lbs.ft of torque at 1,200 rpm. An alternative output of 300 bhp at 1,800 rpm was also available. Within a couple of years and to be compatible with industry practice in offering various power outputs for different applications, the 6LYT could be set to produce 300, 320, 330, 340, or 350 bhp, all at 1,800 rpm. At the maximum power setting torque was 1,140 lbs.ft at 1,200 rpm. The fuel injection system again utilised CAV injectors and a Majormec pump, and followed the pattern established with the 6LXDT. Interestingly, both engines claimed identical minimum specific fuel consumption results.

One major departure from standard Gardner practise featured on the 6LYT was a completely different, rear-mounted gear train. The front mounted timing chain, which dated back to the first LW engines, was finally discarded. The new engine's gear train was driven from a point just forward of the flywheel, known as the nodal point. By locating it there, torsion stresses were either very small or non-

existent, and it was also very quiet. Other innovative features included cross-flow cylinder heads, oil cooled pistons, and the facility for an exhaust brake. On a 6LYT engine the alternator was belt driven, rather than shaft driven as was usual on previous Gardner designs.

A normally aspirated version, 6LY, of the new engine was also available, but it is thought that very few of these were actually made, and only for marine installations. However, in due course a heavy-duty marine propulsion adaptation of the 6LYT was developed and designated YT300. It was set to produce 300 bhp at 1,650 rpm.

At first just 6LXDT engines were fitted into lorries made by ERF, Foden, Seddon Atkinson, and Scammell. It had been customary for all engines to leave Barton Hall painted grey, but the new generation exhibition units received maroon paint. Some luxury coaches built by Neoplan and Plaxton were the first recipients of 6LYT units. Even though the Gardner 6LYT was relatively light in weight for its capacity and power, it did weigh almost 22 hundredweights, which was 4 hundredweights heavier than a 6LXDT. (A 6LYT was still slightly lighter than a Cummins 14 litres engine). Payload conscious lorry purchasers were soon aware of this fact and were reluctant to specify the 6LYT as an option.

The prolonged recession of the early 1980s decimated the remaining British commercial vehicle builders. Foden, and Seddon Atkinson became only peripheral players with very small shares of the market. A Gardner engine was but one power option in these makes. ERF began a long and difficult road to recovery by rationalising its range and introducing its CP models, which stood for "common parts". The aim was to offer standard specification lorries for optimum reliability, performance, economy, and running costs. Building vehicles on the basis of rationalised components was also more cost effective for ERF. Unfortunately for Gardner's, the driveline chosen by ERF for CP lorries was Cummins' lightweight L10 engine at 290 bhp, Fuller gearbox, and Rockwell axles. If an operator did need more power, a 320 bhp version of the Cummins L10 become available, or a Cummins 14 litre engine at 360 bhp could be supplied. ERF was prepared to fit Gardner engines but they carried a hefty surcharge. Within a period of a few months sales of these power units to ERF, once one of the biggest outlets for Barton Hall products, had dwindled to a mere trickle.

There were other difficulties as well. Even though the two new designs, 6LXDT, and 6LYT had been several years evolving, they proved to be underdeveloped because of funding cut backs. Hawker Siddeley was a large organisation, but it had worldwide exposure and suffered in the economic downturn of the eighties and savings had to be made. Research and development was one area where budgets were slashed and the engines were released onto the market with certain problems unresolved. The new Gardner engines encountered faults and failures in service, something never previously associated with Gardner units. Neither type achieved particularly high levels of sales, and when word of breakdowns spread among operators, confidence was badly dented and orders became even harder to win. Spare parts were also difficult to obtain and this exacerbated the situation. Ironically, for the first time in a generation

Gardner's was able to match its competitors on power, but it had fallen behind on reliability. A complete reversal of roles for the Patricroft firm.

It is believed that Hawker Siddeley had been very enthusiastic about the future for Gardner's when it acquired the firm. However, when the serious sales recession of the eighties began to bite, Hawker Siddeley started to lose interest and looked to dispose of its Patricroft division. Many in the industry were surprised when it was announced in 1986 that Hawker Siddeley was selling its Gardner subsidiary to Perkins Engines of Peterborough, itself a division of Massey Ferguson, (later Varity). Perkins Engines was founded by Frank Perkins and his partners in 1932 and initially made high-speed indirect injection diesel engines for replacing petrol units in lightweight commercial vehicles. Early Perkins designs were basic and rather crude if compared with contemporary Gardner's, but they sold into a large, untapped market with huge potential. As sales increased mass production techniques were introduced, which was a very different approach to how things were done at Barton Hall. Eventually Perkins established his engines as optional, or first choice, proprietary fittings in several British makes of light commercials and agricultural tractors, and prospered to become a renowned global supplier of diesels for many applications. Perkins specialised in manufacturing a small range of engines in large numbers. By the mid-eighties Perkins was producing some 385,000 engines annually in its worldwide factories, some one hundredfold more than Gardner's.

Perkins labelled Gardner's as a

specialist engines division and earlier, in 1984, it had acquired the diesel engine designs and Shrewsbury factory of Rolls Royce. This had been an astute move by Perkins, giving it access to the heavy lorry engine market and a range of industrial and battle tank engines with power outputs of up to 1200 bhp. With Gardner's, Perkins now boasted ownership of two of the most prestigious names in premium quality engine manufacturing. But it also meant that two competing brands, viz Rolls and Gardner's, were owned by the same parent company. Both had engines with identical power outputs for lorry applications. However, Gardner's had 75% of the U.K's proprietary bus engine market. This was an area where Perkins, and indeed Rolls, were both weak, but with a potential of just 4,000 units in total annually it only represented a minute percentage of Perkins' output. Because of its very different ranges of mainstream engines and totally opposed production methods there was little Perkins could bring to Gardner's except sales and marketing expertise. No doubt Perkins thought it might revive Gardner's flagging fortunes with the remaining lorry and bus builders, but circumstances had changed quickly and it was very much an uphill struggle.

In the period of Perkins' ownership of Barton Hall Engine Works there was rationalisation of the Gardner range and some re-branding of the 6LXDT. Two marine versions of this engine were introduced, DT250, and DT275. There were also two powerful marine variants of the 6LYT. The first was YT300, and then a turbo-charged and intercooled YTI350. The following table lists Gardner

ENGINE	BHP @ RPM	TORQUE lbs.ft. @ RPM	COMMENTS
6LXB	188 @ 1,850	562 @ 1,000-1,100	Passenger chassis only
230T	230 @ 1,900	700 @ 1,200-1,400	Previously 6LXDT
250T	250 @ 1,900	788 @ 1,200-1,400	Ditto
270T	270 @ 1,900	855 @ 1,200-1,400	Ditto
290T	290 @ 1,900	915 @ 1,200-1,400	Ditto
310T	310 @ 1,900	1000 @ 1,250-1,400	Ditto
6LYT	300 @ 1,800	1,030 @ 1,200	
6LYT	320 @ 1,800	1,030 @ 1,200	
6LYT	330 @ 1,800	1,060 @ 1,200	
6LYT	340 @ 1,800	1,100 @ 1,200	
6LYT	350 @ 1,800	Max.1,140 @ 1,200	
6HLXB	188 @ 1,850	562 @ 1,000-1,100	Horizontal
6HLXCT	242 @ 1,950	673 @ 1,300	Horizontal
6HLXCT	230 @ 1,900	673 @ 1,300	Horizontal
LXB150	150 @ 1,650		6LXB Marine
DT250	250 @ 1,650		6LXDT Marine
DT275	275 @ 1,800		6LXDT Marine
YT300	300 @ 1,650		6LYT Marine
YTI350	350 @ 1,650		Charge-cooled 6LYT Marine

engines available in the first years of the Perkins era. Significantly, Paul Gardner had also resigned within twelve months of the Peterborough based concern taking over.

It can be seen from the above table that Gardner's finally had a range of engines in power bands that were appropriate for all categories of heavy lorries and passenger vehicles. But there were unprecedented changes in the marketplace in the eighties. European and Scandinavian manufacturers increasingly dominated affairs, and the few remaining British chassis builders that bought proprietary engines mainly used Cummins designs. From a position of great strength, Gardner's market had collapsed worryingly in a short period of time. As the 1980s progressed Gardner engines became increasingly rare fitments in chassis.

By 1990 both ERF and Seddon Atkinson had de-listed Gardner engine options from their catalogues; a decision that would have seemed unthinkable ten years before.

In retrospect the changes that occurred in the commercial vehicles and road transport industries in the 1980s were difficult to foresee, and Gardner's was unlucky in encountering problems with new designs at that time. In addition, of its competitors, Cummins in particular had improved its products, and reliability and longevity now matched that of Gardner engines at their best. At higher power outputs there was little or none difference in fuel consumption figures between the new generation Cummins and Gardner designs. Significantly, because Cummins built many more engines annually, its production costs

were much lower and this was reflected in selling prices. Keen competition in every type of road transport operation caused profit margins to narrow, and initial purchasing costs of new vehicles were assiduously studied by accountants and managers before decisions were taken.

Many of the long established Gardner operators in both goods and passenger carrying businesses had sold out to one time rivals or became subsidiaries of large groups. Often these firms had prospered with Gardner engines since the thirties and they were loyal to Barton Hall products. As original owners retired or new managers took over, traditional ways of running businesses were eschewed and Gardner engines became unfashionable in the new order.

CHAPTER

11

IN CONCLUSION

Following decisions by ERF, in particular, and Seddon Atkinson to de-list Gardner engines the available market for Barton Hall's product was seriously restricted. Of the remaining lorry chassis builders only Foden offered its customers an option of Gardner power. This old established firm was still in business, although under the ownership of Paccar of U.S.A. But the potential for supplying engines to Foden was limited. It was registering less than 1,000 vehicles annually on the home market and provided a bespoke chassis specification. A client could choose engines from Cummins, Caterpillar, Rolls Royce, or Gardner. Foden also supplied the Ministry of Defence, but despite Gardner's having the coveted M.o.D. quality standard, AQAP 1, Rolls Royce engines continued to be used in lorries for the British Army.

It was much the same scenario with passenger vehicles. Just as Swedish and European marques totally dominated the commercial vehicles sector, then Volvo, Scania, and DAF also supplied the vast majority of luxury coaches, and of course they made their own engines. Volvo had even purchased the former Leyland bus plant and quite simply there was no market with any substantial sales volume available to

Gardner's. Dennis Brothers of Guildford was still building passenger chassis, and did offer purchasers Gardner engines, but usually Cummins units were specified.

During Perkins' stewardship of Barton Hall some re-development of the new generation engines of 1984 did take place. The 6LXDT was re-worked with a conventional, gear driven camshaft from the front of the crankshaft. As the LG1200 its power range now was from 210 to 275 bhp, with type designations LG210 etc. and the main outlets after the lorry market collapsed became a few passenger chassis builders who needed proprietary engines. One potential outlet was Hong Kong when Dennis won a large order for double deck buses, but there was a disappointing lack of interest in Gardner's and the preferred choice, unfortunately, was Cummins. Only 35 Gardner bus engines were supplied to Hong Kong at this time. A lower power automotive engine still available from Gardner's during the early 1990s was the 6LXB. It was used for buses supplied by Dennis and ERF into African countries where reliability was paramount. By 1992 the famous Gardner 6LXB, for so long the preferred choice of the British bus industry, had to be shelved in its home country because it could not

be made compliant with Euro 1 emissions legislation.

This startling decline in Gardner's fortunes meant that employee numbers were drastically reduced and even parts of Barton Hall were sub-let to tenants with a variety of businesses and trades. Perkins had no future for Gardner's because its Rolls Royce subsidiary was able to supply automotive, rail traction, and industrial engines into any market where a Gardner power unit was an option. Eventually, Perkins disposed of L. Gardner & Sons Ltd. to a Manchester based company called Texas Group, which had previously acquired Gardner's foundry. With hindsight, did Perkins have a hidden agenda for Gardner's from the outset, with eventual run-down planned to protect its Rolls Royce subsidiary?

After over a century in family control, Gardner's was now under its third owner in less than twenty years. Further rationalisation took place and automotive engine production ceased in 1994. This was surely a situation inconceivable only a decade previously. A concerted effort was made to focus on the marine engine market and the range was re-branded retaining a 'LG' prefix designation. In 1996 this became the basis of the Premier Series of marine diesels. Prior to this in 1995 the 2LW engine

ENGINE	POWER RANGE BHP MARINE MAIN	POWER RANGE MARINE AUX.	ORIGIN	NOTES
2LW	28	N/A	LW Series	
LXB	150-175	136-172	6LXB	Normally Aspirated
DT	250-275	227-275	6LXDT	Turbocharged
YT	300-325	275-330	6LYT	Turbocharged
YTI	350-380	318-385	6LYT	Turbo-Intercooled
LG200H	200	N/A	6LXDT	Normally Aspirated
LG225M	225	N/A	6LXDT	Normally Aspirated
LG300H	300	N/A	6LYT	Turbocharged
LG325M	325	N/A	6LYT	Turbocharged
LG350H	350	N/A	6LYT	Turbo-Intercooled
LG380M	380	N/A	6LYT	Turbo-Intercooled
LG400H	400	N/A	6LYT	Turbo-Intercooled
LG420M	420	N/A	6LYT	Turbo-Intercooled

was resurrected as a power unit for inland waterways craft and traditional canal barges. The table above lists the marine engine range advertised.

In addition to supplying Twin Disc marine transmissions Gardner's also listed Tonanco marine gearboxes as alternatives for most of the Premier series.

By the year 1996 Gardner's output was just a fraction of that of its halcyon years. However, there were still thousands of its engines in daily use throughout the world. It was calculated there were almost 60 countries with Gardner engines in service. For supplying spare parts quickly and efficiently a new storage and distribution complex was opened at Barton Hall. Over 9,000 component lines with a value of £5 million were in stock.

At about this time Gardner's affairs and ownership became rather convoluted. In 1995 a totally new investment company with a Stock Exchange listing was formed, calling itself L. Gardner Group PLC. It is understood that the choice of name was purely co-incidental. The main purpose of this holding company was to acquire firms specialising in machining components for the aerospace industry. Texas group, owners of what is best described as Barton Hall Industrial Estate leased the site to L. Gardner Group PLC, and sold them some of its businesses, including the Gardner engine company. Along with the engineering expertise it possessed, Gardner's also had the machinery to make components for aircraft. However, because the marine engine market where Gardner's was active is highly competitive, production of new engines was halted within a couple of years. Needless to say the main suppliers of small and medium sized marine power units similar to Gardner's had become Cummins, Volvo, and Scania. So, after just over a century of being associated with the very best of internal combustion engines, the revered Gardner brand quietly faded away.

A new company named Gardner Avon was formed, but significantly the well-known and distinctive Gardner script logo was retained to promote its activities. Three subdivisions were created comprising Components Supply, Parts and Logistics, and Remanufactured Products. Components division makes precision-machined items such as gears, engine, and transmission parts for aerospace and automotive applications. Parts and Logistics department supplies Gardner engine spares, along with parts for Avon transmissions. Some other under chassis items are also stocked for commercial vehicles.

Gardner Avon Remanufactured Products did originally recondition Gardner engines, along with Leyland and Mercedes units. Some ZF, Voith, and Allison gearboxes were also refurbished. However, at the time of writing (winter 2001/2), it is believed that most of this activity has ceased and some very up-market engines for Rolls Royce and Aston Martin cars are all that are examined and rebuilt now. Incidentally, the last Gardner family member to serve on the Board of Directors, Paul Gardner, eventually established his own company specialising in repairing and reconditioning Gardner engines. The facility therefore exists for those operators still using Gardner engines to have such a unit expertly overhauled.

So as to give some idea of the scale of current trading, for its 2000-2001 financial year L. Gardner Group PLC had a turnover of £124.9 million, but Gardner Avon only contributed approximately £3.0 million, just 2.4% of turnover. The parent company was believed to be considering disposal of its automotive business at the end of 2001 to concentrate on its more profitable aerospace interests.

EPILOGUE

The once common and distinctive sounds produced by Gardner engines are becoming rare as very few Gardner powered lorries remain in everyday service in Great Britain. Several municipal public transport routes throughout the country are still served by buses fitted with Gardner power units, and many of these are now approaching twenty years old. Stagecoach UK alone has one thousand Gardner engined buses. Throughout the world it is the same situation, but all in all there are still thousands of Gardner power units providing reliable and economical service. Many fishing boats, harbour craft, launches, pleasure boats and luxury yachts still rely on Gardner main propulsion, and, or, auxiliary units. In particular Hong Kong remains a stronghold for Barton Hall products with several buses retaining Gardner engines. Here though, the main application is in junks of the harbour and inshore craft of coastal waters. It has long been a Chinese junk owner's ambition to acquire a Gardner engine, usually a second hand example from Great Britain. Such units have covered hundreds of thousands of mile in arduous service before being exported, but after overhaul they are good for more years of hard work. Some well-used engines simply go straight into service.

Amusement caterers and fairground showmen have always favoured Gardner engines, not only for lorries, but also for generating electricity for their rides and sideshows. If you listen to a Gardner LW, LX, or LXB driving a dynamo at 1,500 rpm it is fully on top of its task. As the demand for power increases when a ride starts-up, there is a barely perceptible change in the engine's note as it tackles the load.

Currently there is a flourishing preservation movement in Great Britain and many Gardner engined lorries and buses attend rallies and shows in summer months. In addition to automotive types there are several stationary and industrial Gardner engines in the care of dedicated and enthusiastic owners. Preserved railways also have shunting locomotives with Gardner engines, not only here but also overseas. In recent years Gardner rallies have been organised and there are a couple of societies specifically for Gardner enthusiasts.

Even in the early years of the twenty-first century there is still demand for second hand Gardner engines, although sources are becoming fewer. This was strongly illustrated at an auction sale that took place early in November 2001. A long established haulage firm, G.A. Stamper of Culgaith, Cumbria, was rationalising its operation and decided to dispose of its older assets. Stamper's were staunch Gardner operators for decades and still retained thirteen Seddon Atkinsons and Atkinsons with various types of Gardner engines. All these lorries were out of use and mainly derelict. Nevertheless, six had 8LXB or 8LXC engines and one had an 8LXCT. Every one of them was sold for a sum far in excess of its worth if condition alone was taken into account. The remaining six lorries with Gardner 6LX, 6LXB, or 6LXC units proved to be not quite as desirable, but still attracted much interest. No doubt those with eight-cylinder engines were bought solely for their power units and after refurbishment they would be exported, probably to Hong Kong, Egypt, or the Arabian Gulf, where there is a healthy market for such engines.

During the lengthy heyday of Gardner engines they were superior in most parameters to any similar types, no matter where in the world they were made. Generation after generation of Gardner family members were brilliant designers and engineers and they made pioneering, invaluable, contributions to direct injection diesel engine development. This was in the earliest days of these power units and their innovation continued with the 4LK, 6LX, and its derivatives. The Gardner name will always be associated with engines that were reliable, economical, meticulously engineered, and which gave long operational lives. At the beginning they were inventive by using aluminium and light alloys for lightweight engines, but attention was always paid to technicalities like relative rates of metal expansion. For instance, aluminium expands at a rate three times faster than iron. This is the reason Gardner's fitted oil coolers and insisted on installers providing radiators with large coolant capacities. It was not for nothing that a Gardner engine was always regarded as "a cold engine". If you study a Gardner engine manual, maximum coolant and oil temperatures are stated. Very few competing engine manufacturers had such awareness of details. For most of its existence Gardner's pursued a cheap spare parts policy, thus encouraging operators to rebuild engines after accruing high mileages or running hours. Developments and improvements made since an engine was first built could be incorporated later. For instance, a LW could be uprated to LW20 power and specification.

Tales of Gardner engine achievements and about some of the personalities at Barton Hall are legion. Prodigious mileages approaching 1 millon without overhaul were achieved by LW and LX series engines many years before even half that figure became the industry standard and promoted the Gardner legend of longevity. Engine failures at low mileages were virtually unheard of, causing the company to treat any occasional warranty claims with some suspicion and reluctance. Even the Chief Engineer of the RNLI remarked in a light-hearted fashion on a visit to Patricroft "this is the only supplier I deal with where the customer is always wrong".

Operators showed tremendous loyalty to Gardner engines despite purchase pricing shenanigans by chassis builders. But allegiances could sometimes be sorely tested. One Lancashire based haulier took delivery of a 6LW-powered eight-wheeler only for its crankshaft to snap in two on its first journey to Scotland. Feeling that he had a justifiable warranty claim, the owner approached Barton Hall for a replacement component. He was informed by Hugh Gardner "our crankshafts never break unless seriously abused". To placate their customer and retain his goodwill, the lorry builder bore the cost of the repairs. That haulage contractor was a Gardner man to the core, and bought many more. He used to say "a Gardner engine will always master the driver; a driver can never beat a Gardner". How true it was.

Sadly, the famous Gardner name is now becoming a fond memory of a past era. Like other renowned companies of Britain's commercial vehicles manufacturing and engineering heritage, it represents the highest echelons of this once major industry when it was respected globally. To those of a certain age it is almost incomprehensible that such great firms like L. Gardner & Sons Ltd., Leyland Motors, AEC, Guy, and Daimler, to name just a few, no longer exist. The ground breaking contributions of Gardner's have never been properly recognised and it is hoped that this comprehensive study will go some way to correcting this situation.

In the end times were changing rapidly. That which was universally tried, tested, and proven, became unfashionable and was abandoned by new regimes of owners and operators.

Reliability
Economy
Longevity

These words are synonymous with Gardner engines for posterity.

APPENDIX A

DETAILS OF PRODUCTION RANGE

HORIZONTAL ENGINES

In 1894 the first engine was produced, a type No.1, followed subsequently by numbers 2,3,0,4,1A, 5,6,6/6,7,8,9,10,11,12.

In 1910 engine sizes 0 to 5 became 'F' types, (6 versions), i.e. 1F etc. Larger horizontals became 'H' types, (8 versions), such as 7H and so on. The biggest was a 13H of 70 bhp @ 190 rpm.

In 1898 a small quantity of 2BR petroleum spirit engines were assembled. They had 2-cylinders side by side and were designed for motorcar propulsion. They were probably too expensive for their intended market.

By 1913 'HC' types, (8 versions), followed the 'H' range, these then became 'HF' (11 models), in 1922. There were also one, or possibly two models, of twin 'HF' engines. As well as introducing revised designs it was Gardner's policy to produce original specification engines if customers wanted them. Consequently there was an overlap period of production of all similar and updated types.

Date of last 'F' type: 8th August 1931. (4AF/25398)
Date of last 'H' type: 25th July 1928. (6H/25419)
Date of last 'HC' type: 19th June 1929. (6HC/28145)
Date of last 'HF' type: 10th February 1942. (12HF/54751)

All horizontal industrial engines could be adapted to use every commonly available fuel, such as paraffin, Town Gas, producer gas, benzene, petroleum spirit, alcohol (demineralised methylated spirits), and fuel oil (later known as gas oil, or rebated "red diesel" fuel).

Much later, from 1951, there were horizontal automotive engines, i.e. 4,5, or 6HLW, then 6HLX, 6HLXB, 6HLXCT.

VERTICAL ENGINES

Gardner's produced its first vertical design in 1898, designated 'V' type. The first 'V's were beautiful engines with open crankcases, but enclosed crankcases soon featured. Sizes offered were 0 to 5 with intermediates such as 1A, 2A, etc., probably totalling 11 versions in all.

Multi-cylinder vertical engines with fully enclosed crankshafts became available in late 1902 or early 1903 and these were 'M' types. Initially the range comprised 'MV' versions but it quickly increased to include a plethora of models: 'HV', then 'BM', 'DM', 'FM', 'JM', 'KM', 'NM', 'SM', 'FHM', 'FRM', 'KRM', 'BCM', 'DCM'. Many of them could be specified with varying numbers of cylinders. Usually these were from 1 to 4, but 6-cylinder versions of 'KM' and 'SM' engines could be specified.

The early 'HV' range was either paraffin or petroleum spirit fuelled and for example a single cylinder 'HV' was offered in 9 sizes. Power output was from 5 bhp @ 800 rpm to 35 bhp @ 800 rpm. This was typical Gardner's policy and in the first quarter of the twentieth century they produced an almost bewildering quantity of engine types with optional cylinder dimensions, and varying numbers of cylinders.

Date of last 'V' type: 11th November 1935 (1AV/34577).
Date of last 'M' type: 19th August 1933 (2FHM/30631).

Other important vertical designs were as follows:

'CR' range of petrol engines from 1910. Initially 'CR' and 'ACR' single cylinder units, then 'BCR', 'CCR', and 'DCR' versions with 2, 3, or 4 cylinders.

'TS' engine was a 6-cylinder petrol unit designed by Harry Ricardo for battle tanks in World War One. Gardner's was one of a small number of chosen manufacturers and they also produced all the crankshafts for the few other selected assemblers of these engines.

'RC' engine was a lightweight, high-speed 6-cylinder marine design made in 1918 for torpedo boats. It was pioneering in its extensive use of aluminium alloy metal.

'FD' and 'KD' types, little is known about these at present.

'TP' was a range of 4, 6, or 8-cylinder engines available from 1908.

VEE CONFIGURATION ENGINES

This was a design of engine Gardner's stayed clear of apart from type '2WT', a 2-cylinder Vee configuration. It was air-cooled with 4½ inches cylinder bore and as far as can be deduced '2WT's were only supplied to the General Post Office from 1909 for drying out cable ducts. Amazingly, a single cylinder version, '1WT', was also produced, which was a '2WT' with one power cylinder, the second cylinder being an air compressor.

SEMI-DIESEL ENGINES

These were marine or industrial units using fuel oil and were made to the ideas of combustion propounded by Ackroyd-Stuart, (whose patents pre-dated those of Dr. Diesel by a couple of years), but with improvements implemented by Gardner's. 'VT' types were introduced in 1913 and there was a large range of them.

Single cylinder 'VT's were available in 8 sizes starting at 3.5 bhp @ 500 rpm. Two cylinder types could be ordered in 3 sizes; there were 5 versions of 3-cylinder units; and 4-cylinder 'VT's were also made in 5 sizes. The largest, a 4/8VT produced 120 bhp @ 290 rpm.

'VT's were followed by 'T' types and again could run on either paraffin or fuel oil. There were 6 sizes, namely T4 to T9 inclusive and could be specified with 2, 3, 4, or 6-cylinders.

Twin cylinder 'T's were available in 2 sizes only, 2T7 and 2T8. Three and 4-cylinder versions could be ordered in every size. Six cylinder 'T's were specified in the 2 largest sizes only, 6T8 or 6T9. Power outputs ranged from a 3T4 of 36 bhp @ 450 rpm, to a 6T9 producing 300 bhp @ 290 rpm.

Date of last 'VT'/'T' type: 27th May 1938 (3T4/42248).

COMPRESSION IGNITION ENGINES

Gardner's first true (i.e. dedicated design) compression ignition engine was the 'J' type introduced in 1928. It was a self-reversing two-stroke available with 3,4,5,6,7, or 8-cylinders. Fuel oil was used. Power outputs ranged from 54 to 400 bhp and these were mainly used for marine propulsion or powerhouse generating installations.

Date of last 'J'type: 22nd May 1940 (4J5/49907).

The first four-stroke, high-speed direct injection, compression ignition engine was the L2 introduced in 1929. Originally designed for marine auxiliary and marine propulsion duties, but was used for some automotive and industrial applications. Gardner L2 engines were available with 1,2,3,4,5, or 6-cylinders. A 4L2 was the first British 'oil' engine to be installed in a bus and proved the concept of diesel engine automotive propulsion.

The L2 series was phased out in 1940, but some were made in 1951 for a special customer. Date of last L2: 25th June 1951 (4L2/87122). Note: 1L2 engines remained in production after this date for lightship and lighthouse auxiliary power generation. They were also made in small numbers for oil companies and universities for research projects.

The first purpose built automotive engines were the LW series announced in 1931. Eventually LW engines could be ordered with 2,3,4,5,6, or 8-cylinders and were also used for industrial and marine duties. Horizontal versions were also made.

The Gardner L3 range of industrial, marine, and rail traction engines was introduced in 1932. These engines could have 3,4,5,6, or 8-cylinders and were superseded by the updated L3B designs of 1960. By then the majority of production was 6 and 8-cylinder units.

Date of last L3: 6th December 1961 (8L3/132132).
Date of last 6L3B: 1979
Date of last 8L3B: 1984

A lightweight 4-cylinder 4LK design was announced in 1935, extensively using magnesium and aluminium alloy in manufacture. A limited number of high revving 4LK engines were also made for special applications. 4LKs were mainly automotive engines but some marine versions were made during WWII for midget submarines. One prototype six-cylinder 6LK was made.

The 6LX '150' was introduced in 1958 and further developments of this acclaimed design were the 6LXB '180', (1966), 8LXB, (1970), 6LXC and 8LXC, (both 1978), 6LXCT and 8LXCT, (both 1981). Certain aspects of Gardner 6LXDT and 5LXCT engines (both 1984) can also be attributed to the 6LX. Principally they were automotive power units, but marine and industrial versions of most of these designs were also produced. Horizontal 6-cylinder variants were also available for under floor passenger chassis applications.

The final Gardner engine designs were based on brand new 6LYT and 6LY ranges introduced in 1984. These were for automotive, marine, and industrial duties. Following the various takeovers of Gardner's some re-branding took place, i.e. a 6LXDT engine became a 290T for example, then LG1200. The 6LYT range became LG400. For further details refer to chapters 10, 11, and Appendix C.

For more information about cylinder dimensions and power outputs of the main compression-ignition engines produced from 1929 see Appendix C.

OTHER GARDNER PRODUCTS

DYNAMOES. Total production was approximately 160 between 1892 and 1901. Available in 18 sizes from 100 to 24,000 watts. Armature sizes ranged from 2¾ inches to 14¾ inches. A least one electric motor was made.

MACHINE TOOLS. Principally crankpin turning machines for internal use at Barton Hall and they were also sold to virtually every other engine maker in Great Britain in the early years of the twentieth century. Such prestigious names as Rolls Royce bought this machinery, which was available in 3 sizes. They were also exported to Europe and Russia. Gardner's also made most of the other plant and equipment for its factories, including Barton Hall Engine Works.

GAS PRODUCERS. Probably 4 different sizes from 48 bhp to 150 bhp.

WATER PUMPS. Single acting and double acting pumps for marine and industrial use.

AIR COMPRESSORS. Types 'OVC', 'TS1', and 'TS2' compressors, usually for starting the larger Gardner marine and industrial engines.

MUNITIONS. Mainly in the First World War, gun carriages and shell casings, but also some in WWII including components for anti-aircraft guns.

MARINE REVERSE GEAR. Available in various sizes depending on marine engine power rating. Also types 'GT', 'Conic', 'UC2', and 'UC3'. (UC = Unit Construction, bolted directly onto engine).

MARINE STERN GEAR. In the 1920s Gardner's made stern gear including shafting, and even variable pitch screw propellers.

MISCELLANEOUS. Mainly from the first thirty years of Gardner's existence. Items recorded include dentist chairs, coffee roasters (2 sizes), boot sewing machines, dovetailing machinery, bread dough mixers, cardboard folding machines, ink feeders for printing machine rollers, Robinson Hot Air Engines (3 sizes), and components for Robinson Gas Engines. This involvement with Robinson's caused Gardner's to design its own engines.

APPENDIX B

VALUE OF ENGINES PRODUCED 1915–1933

YEAR	HORIZONTAL ENGINES MADE	TOTAL VALUE £	AVE. VALUE £	VERTICAL ENGINES MADE	TOTAL VALUE £	AVE. VALUE £	GRAND TOTAL ENGINES	GRAND TOTAL £	AVE. ENGINE VALUE £
1915	220	9,597	43.62	916	72,486	79.13	1,136	82,083	72.26
1916	237	13,990	59.02	824	72,249	87.68	1,061	86,239	81.28
1917	95	6,852	72.13	604	125,263	207.39	699	132,115	189.01
1918	31	2,176	70.19	360	152,319	423.11	391	154,495	395.13
1919	218	20,698	94.94	808	123,619	152.99	1,026	144,317	140.66
1920	373	47,751	128.01	546	73,876	135.30	919	121,627	132.35
1921	152	22,325	146.88	219	43,674	199.42	371	65,999	177.89
1922	175	21,023	120.13	322	34,455	107.00	497	55,478	111.63
1923	61	7,155	117.30	229	27,405	119.67	290	34,560	119.17
1924	87	14,977	172.15	322	49,088	152.45	409	64,065	156.64
1925	169	35,418	209.57	340	84,195	247.63	509	119,613	235.00
1926	150	31,372	209.15	303	62,832	207.37	453	94,204	207.96
1927	125	28,588	228.70	287	88,004	306.63	412	116,592	282.99
1928	166	35,914	216.35	315	96,142	305.21	481	132,056	274.54
1929	127	31,084	244.76	284	117,903	415.15	411	148,987	362.50
1930	79	18,118	229.34	436	176,901	405.74	515	195,019	378.68
1931	55	15,571	283.11	411	123,252	299.88	466	138,823	297.90
1932	39	11,881	304.64	695	252,714	363.62	734	264,595	360.48
1933	32	6,418	200.56	904	302,450	334.57	936	308,868	329.99

NOTE: From this table it is apparent that vertical engines had higher monetary values than horizontal types. The impact on average values of tank engine production in the latter part of WWI is noticeable. Also, Gardner's were certainly struggling in the mid-1920s and it obvious that their new direct injection compression ignition engines were absolutely vital for the future prosperity of the company. In less than 20 years unit values increased almost fivefold as a result of the new types.

APPENDIX C

HIGH SPEED DIESEL ENGINES POWER OUTPUTS AND RATINGS

NOTE: Brake horse power (bhp) outputs and ratings quoted are as stated by Gardner's when the engines were in production. Normally outputs were established at British Standard criteria of 29.92 inches of mercury atmospheric pressure and 60 degrees Farenheit temperature.

From 1972, dual imperial and metric power ratings were used in Great Britain; engine power output in bhp and kilo-Watts (kW), torque in lbs.ft., and Newton metres (Nm).

To convert bhp to kW, multiply bhp value by 0.746. To convert lbs.ft. to Nm, multiply lbs.ft. value by 1.355.

Marine Rating 1 was for heavy-duty applications.
Marine Rating 2 was for yachts and luxury cruisers.
Marine Rating 3 was for high-speed craft.
Industrial Rating 1 was constant speed running as for electricity generation.
Industrial Rating 2 was for intermediate duties such as air compressors, pumping, drilling rigs, excavators, and sawmills etc.

L2 SERIES INTRODUCED 1929

Cylinder dimensions: 4¼ inches bore by 6 inches stroke, (or 107.95 mm x 152.4 mm).

TYPE	SWEPT VOL. cu.ins.	SWEPT VOL. Litres	AUTOMOTIVE bhp	AUTOMOTIVE rpm	RAIL TRACTION bhp	RAIL TRACTION rpm	MARINE 1 bhp	MARINE 1 rpm	MARINE 2 bhp	MARINE 2 rpm	MARINE 3 bhp	MARINE 3 rpm	INDUSTRIAL 1 bhp	INDUSTRIAL 1 rpm	INDUSTRIAL 2 bhp	INDUSTRIAL 2 rpm
1L2*	85	1.395	-	-	-	-	-	-	-	-	-	-	11	1100	-	-
2L2	170	2.790	-	-	-	-	19	1000	23	1200	24.5	1300	21	1100	23	1200
3L2	255	4.184	-	-	-	-	28.5	1000	34	1200	37	1300	31	1100	34	1200
4L2	340	5.579	50	1300	38	1000	38	1000	46	1200	50	1300	42	1100	46	1200
5L2	426	6.974	61.5	1300	47.5	1000	47.5	1000	57	1200	61.5	1300	52	1100	57	1200
6L2	511	8.369	74	1300	57	1000	57	1000	68	1200	74	1300	63	1100	68	1200

Maximum Torque For Automotive Applications:
4L2: 215 lbs.ft., 5L2: 265 lbs.ft., 6L2: 314 lbs.ft., all @ 1000 rpm.

NOTE: *1L2 Laboratory type engine rated at 16 bhp @ 1600 rpm.

Intermittent duty ratings were increased in 1940 to maximums:
2L2, - 26 bhp @ 1300 rpm and 108 lbs.ft. @ 1000 rpm.
3L2, - 39 bhp @ 1300 rpm and 163 lbs.ft. @ 1000 rpm.
4L2, - 52 bhp @ 1300 rpm and 217 lbs.ft. @ 1000 rpm.
5L2, - 65 bhp @ 1300 rpm and 270 lbs.ft. @ 1000 rpm.
6L2, - 78 bhp @ 1300 rpm and 326 lbs.ft. @ 1000 rpm.

LW SERIES INTRODUCED 1931

Cylinder dimensions: 4¼ inches bore by 6 inches stroke, (or 107.95 mm x 152.4 mm).

TYPE	SWEPT VOL. cu.ins.	SWEPT VOL. Litres	AUTOMOTIVE bhp	AUTOMOTIVE rpm	RAIL TRACTION bhp	RAIL TRACTION rpm	MARINE 1 bhp	MARINE 1 rpm	MARINE 2 bhp	MARINE 2 rpm	MARINE 3 bhp	MARINE 3 rpm	INDUSTRIAL 1 bhp	INDUSTRIAL 1 rpm	INDUSTRIAL 2 bhp	INDUSTRIAL 2 rpm
2LW	170	2.79	-	-	35.5	1700	24*	1200*	30	1500	-	-	24	1200	29	1400
3LW	255	4.184	-	-	53.5	1700	36	1200	45	1500	-	-	36	1200	43	1400
4LW	340	5.579	68/75K	1700	71	1700	56	1300	62	1500	71	1700	48	1200	58	1400
5LW	426	6.974	85/94K	1700	88	1700	70	1300	78	1500	89	1700	60	1200	72	1400
6LW	511	8.369	102/112K	1700	107	1700	84	1300	94	1500	107	1700	72	1200	87	1400
8LW	680	11.158	140/150K	1700	-	-	112	1300	124	1500	140	1700	-	-	-	-
5LW20	426	6.974	100/104#	1700	100	1700	-	-	-	-	-	-	-	-	-	-
6LW20	511	8.369	120/125#	1700	120	1700	-	-	-	-	-	-	-	-	-	-

Maximum Torque For Automotive Applications:
4LW: 232 lbs.ft. @ 1000 rpm.
4LWK: 237 lbs.ft. @ 1300 rpm.
5LW: 285 lbs.ft. @ 1000 rpm.
5LWK: 300 lbs.ft. @ 1300 rpm.
5LW/20: 317 lbs.ft. @ 1350 rpm. (327 lbs.ft. BSAU 141a 1971)
6LW: 348 lbs.ft. @ 1000 rpm.
6LWK: 358 lbs.ft. @ 1300 rpm.
6LW/20: 381 lbs.ft. @ 1350rpm. (390 lbs.ft. BSAU 141a 1971)
8LW: 458 lbs.ft. @ 1000 rpm.
8LWK: 478 lbs.ft. @ 1300 rpm.

NOTES:
(A) * The 2LW engine was re-introduced in 1995 for powering inland waterways craft and traditional canal barges. Power output was 28 bhp @ 1300 rpm.
(B) # LW20s were also rated to BSAU 141a 1971 standards to the second figure quoted.
(C) K Type engines were introduced in 1950 offering up to 18.7 bhp per cylinder as a result of fuel injection, breathing, and piston developments.
(D) LW20 engines, (20 bhp per cylinder) were introduced in 1968 following further fuel injection, breathing, and piston developments.
(E) Horizontal automotive variants 4HLW, 5HLW, and 6HLW were all K types and had identical power ratings as vertical engines of the same cylinder configuration. Whilst a spare parts catalogue showing 5HLW20 and 6HLW20 components was issued, no horizontal engines to this specification were actually built.

L. GARDNER & SONS LIMITED

L3 SERIES INTRODUCED 1932

Cylinder dimensions: 5½ inches bore by 7¾ inches stroke, (or 139.7 mm x 196.8 mm).

TYPE	SWEPT VOL. cu.ins.	Litres	AUTOMOTIVE bhp	rpm	RAIL TRACTION bhp	rpm	MARINE 1 bhp	rpm	MARINE 2 bhp	rpm	MARINE 3 bhp	rpm	INDUSTRIAL 1 bhp	rpm	INDUSTRIAL 2 bhp	rpm
3L3	552	9.066	-	-	-	-	48/56	800/900	68	1100	74	1200	55	900	68	1100
4L3	736	12.079	-	-	102	1200	63/75	800/900	92	1100	100	1200	75	900	100	1100
5L3	921	15.115	-	-	128	1200	79/93	800/900	115	1100	125	1200	95	900	125	1100
6L3	1105	18.135	-	-	153	1200	95/112	800/900	135	1100	150	1200	115	900	135	1100
8L3	1473	24.175	-	-	204	1200	126/150	800/900	180	1100	200	1200	150	900	180	1100
6L3B	1105	18.135	-	-	195	1300	150	1000	172	1150	195	1300	139	1000	158	1100
8L3B	1473	24.175	-	-	260	1300	200	1000	230	1150	260	1300	185	1000	210	1100

Maximum Torque For Rail Traction Applications:
4L3: 488 lbs.ft. @ 700 rpm.
5L3: 610 lbs.ft. @ 700 rpm.
6L3: 733 lbs.ft @ 700 rpm. (6L3B: 823 lbs.ft. @ 850 rpm).
8L3: 978 lbs.ft. @ 700 rpm. (8L3B:1097 lbs.ft. @ 850 rpm).

4LK ENGINE INTRODUCED 1935

Cylinder dimensions: 3¾ inches bore by 5¼ inches stroke, (or 95.3 mm x 133.4 mm).

TYPE	SWEPT VOL. cu.ins.	Litres	AUTOMOTIVE bhp	rpm	RAIL TRACTION bhp	rpm	MARINE 1 bhp	rpm	MARINE 2 bhp	rpm	MARINE 3 bhp	rpm	INDUSTRIAL 1 bhp	rpm	INDUSTRIAL 2 bhp	rpm
4LK*	232	3.80	53	2000	-	-	-	-	-	-	-	-	-	-	-	-
4LK	232	3.80	57	2100	-	-	42	1500	51	1800	60	2100	-	-	-	-
4LK Car	232	3.80	85	3000	-	-	-	-	-	-	-	-	-	-	-	-
4LK#	232	3.80	60	2100	-	-	-	-	-	-	-	-	-	-	-	-

Maximum Torque For Automotive Applications:
4LK*: 147 lbs.ft. @ 1200 rpm. (original pre-war specification)
4LK: 161 lbs.ft. @ 900/1300 rpm.
4LK Car 175 lbs.ft. @ 1000 rpm.
4LK#: 162 lbs.ft. @ 1100 rpm. (from 1960 onwards)

NOTE: 4LK Car denotes the special high performance version made in limited numbers for private cars.

6LX SERIES INTRODUCED 1958

Cylinder dimensions: 4¾ inches bore by 6 inches stroke, (or 120.7 mm x 152.4 mm).

TYPE	SWEPT VOL. cu.ins.	Litres	AUTOMOTIVE bhp	rpm	RAIL TRACTION bhp	rpm	MARINE 1 bhp	rpm	MARINE 2 bhp	rpm	MARINE 3 bhp	rpm	INDUSTRIAL 1 bhp	rpm	INDUSTRIAL 2 bhp	rpm
6LX	638	10.45	150/157*	1700	150	1700	110	1300	127	1500	144	1700	97	1200	119	1400
6HLX	638	10.45	150/157*	1700	150	1700	-	-	-	-	-	-	-	-	-	-
6LXB	638	10.45	180/188*	1850	180	1850	127	1500	150/127	1500	140	1700	115	1200	140	1400
6HLXB	638	10.45	180/188*	1850	180	1850	-	-	-	-	-	-	-	-	-	-
8LXB	851	13.93	240/250*	1850	-	-	153	1300	170	1500	200	1700	150	1200	185	1400
6LXC	638	10.45	193/201*	1920	-	-	-	-	-	-	-	-	-	-	-	-
8LXC	851	13.93	255/265*	1920	-	-	-	-	-	-	-	-	-	-	-	-
6LXCT	638	10.45	220/230*	1900	-	-	-	-	-	-	-	-	-	-	-	-
6HLXCT	638	10.45	220/230*	1900	-	-	-	-	-	-	-	-	-	-	-	-
8LXCT	851	13.93	290/300*	1900	-	-	-	-	-	-	-	-	-	-	-	-
5LXCT	532	8.71	185/170#	1900	-	-	-	-	-	-	-	-	-	-	-	-
LXB	638	10.45	-	-	-	-	150	1650	-	-	175	1800	136	1500	150	1500

Maximum Torque For Vertical And Horizontal Automotive Applications:
6LX: 485 lbs.ft. @ 1050 rpm.
6LXB: 536 lbs.ft. @ 1050 rpm. 562 lbs.ft. @ 1000 rpm.*
8LXB: 695 lbs.ft @ 1050 rpm. 728 lbs.ft. @ 1000 rpm.*
6LXC: 553/579* lbs.ft. @ 1100 rpm.
8LXC: 722/752* lbs.ft. @ 1000 rpm.
6LXCT: 673 lbs.ft. @ 1400 rpm. (B.S.) 650 lbs.ft. @ 1400 rpm test bed.
8LXCT: 880 lbs.ft. @ 1400 rpm. (B.S.) 865 lbs.ft. @ 1400 rpm test bed.
5LXCT: 560 lbs.ft. @1300 rpm. Test bed & E.C.

NOTE:
* Second value denotes BSAU 141a 1971 Rating.
# 5LXCT 170 bhp @ 1850 rpm.
6HLXCT also available at coach rating of 234/242* bhp @ 1950 rpm.

6LXDT ENGINE SERIES INTRODUCED 1984

Cylinder dimensions: 5.125 inches bore by 6.25 inches stroke, (or 130.17 mm x 158.75 mm).

TYPE	SWEPT VOL. cu.ins. Litres	AUTOMOTIVE bhp rpm	RAIL TRACTION bhp rpm	MARINE 1 bhp rpm	MARINE 2 bhp rpm	MARINE 3 bhp rpm	INDUSTRIAL 1 bhp rpm	INDUSTRIAL 2 bhp rpm
6LXDT	775 12.68	230-270 1900	- -	- -	- -	- -	- -	- -
230T	775 12.68	230 1900	- -	- -	- -	- -	- -	- -
250T	775 12.68	250 1900	- -	- -	- -	- -	- -	- -
270T	775 12.68	270 1900	- -	- -	- -	- -	- -	- -
290T	775 12.68	290 1900	- -	- -	- -	- -	- -	- -
310T	775 12.68	310 1900	- -	- -	- -	- -	- -	- -
LG200H	775 12.68	- -	- -	200 1650	- -	- -	- -	- -
LG225M	775 12.68	- -	- -	- -	225 1800	- -	- -	- -
LG1200	775 12.68	210-275 1900	- -	- -	- -	- -	- -	- -
DT250	775 12.68	- -	- -	250 1650	- -	- -	227 1500	- -
DT275	775 12.68	- -	- -	- -	- -	275 1800	- -	275 1800

Maximum Torque For Automotive Applications:
6LXDT: 700 to 855 lbs.ft. @ 1300 rpm.
230T: 700 lbs.ft. @ 1300 rpm.
250T: 788 lbs.ft. @ 1300 rpm.
270T: 855 lbs.ft. @ 1300 rpm.
290T: 915 lbs.ft. @ 1350 rpm.
310T: 1000 lbs.ft. @ 1350 rpm.
LG1200: 680 lbs.ft to 865 lbs.ft. @ 1300 to 1400 rpm.

NOTE:
Industrial power ratings apply for Marine Auxiliary duties.

6LYT ENGINE SERIES INTRODUCED 1984

Cylinder dimensions: 5.51 inches bore by 6.61 inches stroke, (or 140 mm x 168 mm).

TYPE	SWEPT VOL. cu.ins. Litres	AUTOMOTIVE bhp rpm	RAIL TRACTION bhp rpm	MARINE 1 bhp rpm	MARINE 2 bhp rpm	MARINE 3 bhp rpm	INDUSTRIAL 1 bhp rpm	INDUSTRIAL 2 bhp rpm
6LYT	946 15.49	300-350 1800	- -	- -	- -	- -	- -	- -
YT	946 15.49	- -	- -	300 1650	- -	325 1800	275 1500	300 1500
YTI	946 15.49	- -	- -	350 1650	- -	380 1800	318 1500	350 1500
LG300H	946 15.49	- -	- -	300 1650	- -	- -	275 1500	- -
LG325M	946 15.49	- -	- -	- -	325 1800	- -	300 1500	- -
LG350H	946 15.49	- -	- -	350 1650	- -	- -	325 1500	- -
LG380M	946 15.49	- -	- -	- -	380 1800	- -	350 1500	- -
LG400H	946 15.49	- -	- -	400 1650	- -	- -	375 1500	- -
LG420M	946 15.49	- -	- -	- -	420 1800	- -	385 1800	- -

Maximum Torque For Automotive Applications:
6LYT300: 1030 lbs.ft. @ 1200 rpm.
6LYT320: 1030 lbs.ft. @ 1200 rpm.
6LYT330: 1060 lbs.ft. @ 1200 rpm.
6LYT340: 1100 lbs.ft. @ 1200 rpm.
6LYT350: 1140 lbs.ft. @ 1200 rpm.

NOTE:
Industrial 1 power ratings apply for Marine Auxiliary duties.

APPENDIX D

ANNUAL ENGINE PRODUCTION

YEAR	TOTAL	YEAR	TOTAL	YEAR	TOTAL
1894	21	1925	509	1956	5,033
1895	68	1926	453	1957	4,289
1896	105	1927	412	1958	3,225
1897	197	1928	481	1959	3,793
1898	295	1929	411	1960	4,600
1899	410	1930	515	1961	4,631
1900	469	1931	466	1962	4,508
1901	473	1932	734	1963	4,712
1902	480	1933	936	1964	4,724
1903	785	1934	1,860	1965	4,505
1904	839	1935	1,983	1966	4,433
1905	902	1936	2,862	1967	5,021
1906	907	1937	3,548	1968	5,329
1907	1,182	1938	3,935	1969	5,560
1908	1,105	1939	3,560	1970	5,707
1909	1,766	1940	2,947	1971	6,189
1910	1,623	1941	2,741	1972	5,680
1911	2,197	1942	2,967	1973	2,937
1912	1,915	1943	3,297	1974	3,479
1913	1,822	1944	3,421	1975	3,868
1914	1,215	1945	3,219	1976	4,525
1915	1,136	1946	3,378	1977	5,271
1916	1,061	1947	3,265	1978	5,754
1917	699	1948	3,713	1979	5,499
1918	391	1949	3,854		
1919	1,026	1950	3,712		
1920	919	1951	4,027		
1921	371	1952	4,178		
1922	497	1953	4,143		
1923	290	1954	4,633		
1924	409	1955	4,552		

QUANTITIES OF HIGH SPEED DIESEL ENGINES DESPATCHED FROM INTRODUCTION UNTIL END OF 1979

TYPE	TOTAL
LW SERIES	90,565
LW20s	1,434
4LK	6,279
HLW	4,838
6LX	30,004
6HLX	2,760
6LXB	34,420
6HLXB	875
8LXB	5,494
6LXC	2,460
8LXC	919
6LXCT	3
L2	3,410
L3	4,596
6L3B	795
8L3B	1,578
GRAND TOTAL	190,430

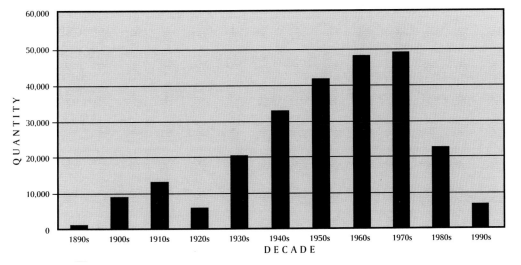

ENGINE PRODUCTION BY DECADE

205

ENGINES SUPPLIED TO CHASSIS MAKERS 1937–1975

YEAR	ATKINSON	BRISTOL	DAIMLER	ERF	FODEN	GUY	SCAMMELL	SEDDON	DENNIS
1937	46	443	488	355	No data	15	184	-	14
1938	82	294	212	418	382	30	474	-	26
1939	66	662	451	431	499	4	328	-	62
1940	82	294	212	418	382	30	474	-	26
1946	97	302	345	320	591	701	109	-	No data
1947	121	283	377	342	623	723	115	-	No data
1948	139	269	401	333	695	747	78	-	No data
1949	159	273	365	343	742	762	93	-	27
1950	262	421	177	353	747	607	66	-	7
1951	325	218	241	359	662	611	110	-	-
1952	382	306	265	375	621	733	103	-	-
1953	355	353	437	438	597	541	164	-	-
1954	469	407	162	400	637	620	121	-	-
1955	419	417	167	412	575	696	85	-	-
1956	540	528	351	476	712	594	130	83	-
1957	349	539	202	436	585	524	89	86	-
1958	327	515	152	273	464	275	49	57	-
1959	403	626	156	452	603	335	74	64	-
1960	504	486	100	509	713	399	164	73	-
1961	590	533	271	613	794	238	191	96	-
1962	612	645	378	641	762	288	207	77	-
1963	709	517	565	697	752	401	88	23	-
1964	743	496	475	665	725	474	65	151	-
1965	695	568	538	580	661	434	62	114	-
1966	711	513	577	587	683	398	15	144	-
1967	780	568	731	679	775	443	16	176	-
1968	883	534	491	1,036	776	732	41	102	-
1969	895	485	712	1,167	841	593	111	183	-
1970	883	482	812	1,219	870	522	120	247	-
1971	1,036	482	895	1,283	902	525	98	373	-
1972	877	386	797	1,164	1,004	680	70	221	-
1973	424	247	333	586	521	270	45	129	-
1974	475	371	233*	733	581	298	10	247	-
1975	525	395	481*	875	527	395	-	271	-

NOTES:

A. Despite Seddon acquiring Atkinson in 1970, between that date and 1975 production of both vehicle types continued separately at Oldham and Walton-le-Dale respectively, hence individual listings for each marque.

B. * Supplied to British Leyland Group for bus power units.

C. Records show that AEC bought the following quantity of Gardner engines:
1937: 21,
1938: 44,
and 1939: 70.

D. There are no records of engines supplied to civilian customers for 1941 to 1945 inclusive. Allocation was by the Ministry of Supply mainly to Guy, Foden, ERF (limited number), and Atkinson (also limited quantity).

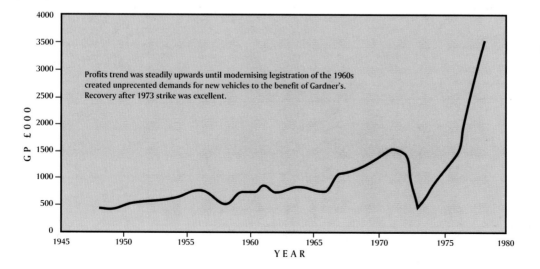

Profits trend was steadily upwards until modernising legistration of the 1960s created unprecented demands for new vehicles to the benefit of Gardner's. Recovery after 1973 strike was excellent.

YEAR

ANNUAL GROSS PROFIT BEFORE TAXATION 1948–1978

INDEX

A

Ackroyd-Stuart, Herbert 35,57
AEC 68, 74-75, 81-82, 89,
   121-122, 128, 135-139, 141,
   162, 165, 168, 171, 190, 198
Albion Motors 85, 89-90, 108, 137
Allens 102
Annual engine production 205
Armstrong Whitworth 25
Atkinson 89, 102, 111, 121,
   123-124, 126, 128, 136, 137,
   138, 147, 155, 159, 162,
   164-165, 167, 171-172,
   175-176, 197, ii, iii, vi
Austin 52
Avonside Engine Co. 79

B

Bagnalls 89
Bailey, William 121, 124
Ball, Mr 103
Barton, Trevor 70-71, 73-74
Bedford 127, 148, 162
Benn, Tony, M.P. 179
Bentley car 98-99, 101, 103
Bentley, W.O. 98-99
Benz, Karl 10
Bernard 92, 107
Boothby, Robert, M.P. 131
Bosch 66, 69
Bradford City Tramways 85
Bradshaw, Eric 133, 136, 158
Bristol 86, 90, 111, 122, 130,
   136, 138, 153, 159, 151-162,
   176, 184, 189, 191
British Leyland Group 171
British Railways 123
Brooks, F. 172
Broom & Wade 131
Brotherhood, Peter 52
Brown, David 86, 90, 122, 124,
   147
BRS 123, 128, 138, 141, 162
Brunel, Isambard 6
Bugatti, Ettore 98

C

Camper & Nicholson 69
Caterpillar 141
CAV 69, 184, 111, 191-192
Chassis makers' engines table
   206
Connor, Peter 182
Corbitt 144
County Donegal Railway Co. 95
Crank pin turning machines
   52-54
Crossley, Sir Kenneth 47
Crossley 13, 55, 73-74, 80, 90
Cummins 141, 162, 164, 171,
   173, 175-177, 188-189, 192-196

D

DAF 176, 195
Daimler 52, 122, 159, 176, 189,
   191
Denholm, D. M. (Dan) 47, 124,
   133
Dennis 89-90, 139, 176, 190,
   192, 195
Diesel Services Pty Ltd. 167
Diesel, Dr. Rudolf 35, 37, 57
Dodwell 62, 165
Dorman 52, 89-90
Drewry 78, 104, 123
Dumoulin-Nagent 47
Dutsons 72-73
Dynamo production 10-11

E

Emu Bay Railway 82
Engines maintenance cost
comparisons 189
Engine pricing 188
Engines range – Perkins
   ownership 194
Engine Types: (In chronological
   sequence of development)
   Appendix A 199-200
   Appendix C 202-204
   Early horizontals 13-15, 28
   Early verticals 19,21
   '2BR' 21
   'V' Type 21, 28, 44, 95
   'M' Series 21-22, 26, 28-29, 44,
      93, 154, 163
   'HV' 22
   'CR' 27, 29-32, 44, 95
   'H' 28, 37, 39, 64
   'TP' 28
   '2WT' 28
   'F' 28, 34-35, 93
   'T' 29, 32, 34, 37, 39-40,
      47-48, 59, 95
   'VT' 29, 32, 34, 37-38, 40, 44,
      95
   'HC' 37-39, 64
   'TS' 51, 54-55
   'HF' 56-57, 59, 63-65, 111
   'RC' 57
   'J' 59-62, 66, 90, 107, 111
   'OVC' 59, 63, 124
   L2 68-79, 81-83, 85, 89-90, 95,
      111, 113-115, 118, 124,
      151, 180, 187
   LW 78, 81-83, 85-87, 89-90,
      92-93, 95, 97-99, 101-103,
      106, 109, 111, 113-116,
      118-120, 122, 124-125,
      127-133, 137-139, 141-149,
      151, 153, 156, 161-162,
      165-168, 171, 178-180,
      195, 197-198, i, iii, vii
   L3 93-97, 104, 106-107, 111,
      113, 117-119, 122, 124-125,
      149-150, 153-155, 157, 178
   LK 96-98, 101, 103, 111-112,
      120, 124, 148, 160, 166,
      178, 197
   6LX 133-136, 138, 141,
      144-146, 153-154, 164-167,
      169, 171-173, 180, 197-198,
      iii, v,vi
   L3B 153-155,162 165, 167,
      170, 180
   LXB 166-168, 171, 173-175,
      177, 182-184, 186-188,
      190, 195, 197, ii, iii, v, vi
   LXC 187, 190, 197
   LXCT 190-192, 197, vi
   6LXDT & DT Series 191-193,
      195-196, v
   6LY 183, 192, 196
   6LYT & YT Series 192, 196, iv,
      viii
   LG Series 195-196
   Premier Marine Series 195-196
   LX Series power outputs 190
ERF 89, 97, 102, 111, 120-121,
   123-124, 128, 130, 136-137,
   147, 155, 159, 161, 164-165,
   171, 175-176, 184, 188,
   190-192, 193-195, ii, v
Estimated engine requirements
   1979 189

F

F.N. 92
Faraday, Michael 10
Ferry Engine Co. 131
Flint, Clayton 181, 183-184,
   187-188
Foden 81, 86, 90, 97, 102, 111,
   120, 123, 126, 128, 136-137,
   155, 162, 164-166, 169, 171,
   175-176, 190-192, 195, ii, iii, iv
Foden, Edwin R. 89, 130
Fuel savings comparison 188

G

Gardner Avon 196
Gardner Engines (Sales) Ltd. 121,
   155
Gardner Engines (South Africa)
   Ltd. 136
Gardner Engines Ireland Ltd. 95
Gardner Engines S.A. 136
Gardner Family:
   Anne 8-9, 11
   Dorothy 7
   Edward 7, 9, 11, 13-14, 17, 35,
      47-48, 111, 120
   Elizabeth 7, 109, 158
   Eric 7, 98, 109, 111, 124
   Ernest 7, 48
   Hugh 7, 65, 69, 98, 101, 109,
      118, 121, 124, 128,
      130-132, 141, 145, 155,
      158-159, 164, 166, 172,
      175, 178, 180-182, 187,
      190, 198
   Jane Jnr. 7
   Jane Snr. 6
   John 7, 65, 69, 98, 109, 121,
      124, 129, 130-132, 141,
      145, 155, 158-159, 172,
      175, 180-183, 187
   Joseph 7, 47-48, 52, 55, 65,
      69, 71, 98, 111, 120, 124,
      133
   Lawrence Jnr. 8, 48
   Lawrence Snr. 6-7, 65, 109, 124
   Paul 131, 159, 181-183, 187,
      190, 194, 196
   Robert 8
   Teddy 8
   Thomas Jnr. (Mr Tom) 7, 9,
      11-14, 17, 35, 42, 48-49,
      69, 71, 92, 95, 98, 109, 111
   Thomas Snr. 6
   Tommy 8
   William 8, 18, 48, 124
Gardner products 200
Gardner, L. Group Plc 196
Gleniffer 70-71, 113
Goedicke, Eduard 47
Great Northern Railway 104
Grove, Harry 42
Guy Motors 78, 81, 86, 89, 90,
   120, 122, 136-137, 139-140,
   159, 162, 164-165, 173, 176,
   191, 198

H

Hanson 183
Hawker Siddeley 177, 183-184,
   187, 190-191, 193, i
Hawker Siddeley takeover
   proposals 185
Hayes Anderson 142
Heath, Edward, M.P. 178
Henty, Alfred 18
Henty, Capt. Charles 18, 42, 95
Houghton, Dion 121, 137, 172,
   182, 187
Houghton, Gordon 47, 90, 137
Howard de Clifford, The Lord
   101
Howarth, Geoff 182, 187
Huddersfield Corporation 76
Hudswell Clarke 74, 95, 123
Hunslet 106, 123, 157
Hunter, H. E. (Harry) 47, 55
Huwood-Hudswell 156

I

Industry Act 1972 181
Ingersoll-Rand 132
Invicta 97, 103

J

Jaguar 103, 160, 171

K

Karrier Motors 74, 76, 78, 81, 86
Kenworth 142
Kromhout 92, 107
Kuwait, Sheik of 146
Kynaston, Anne 6

L

L.G.O.C. 81
L.U.T. 139
Lacy-Hulbert & Co. 52
Lagonda 97, 103
Laird Group 183
Lanchester 52
Lancia 70-71, 73
Latil 92, 97
Le Combe 47
Leeds City Transport 73, 80-81
Levoir 10
Leyland Motors 68, 72, 75,
    81-82, 85, 122, 128, 136-139,
    141, 153, 162, 165, 168, 183,
    186, 189, 190-192, 195-196,
    198
Lister 55, 190, i
LMS Railways 76
London Transport 168,190
Lyons, William 160

M

Mack 141, 143-144
Maddox, W.R.W. 182
Manchester Corporation
Transport 74, 80
**Marine engine installations &
references:**
    "Aloha" 90
    "Baba" 154
    "Cachabol" 104
    "Duchess" 32
    "Faithful" 163
    "Foxton" 153
    "George Urie Scott" 151
    "Gleaner" 154
    "Kiloran" 74
    "Kusa" 149
    "Kwang Su" 31
    "Lady Of The Isles" 104
    "Lochinver" 26
    "Maggie Janes" 163
    "Mascot" 32
    "Mirimar" 90
    "Mola-Mola" 153
    "Nasir" 62

    "Nivanga" 165
    "Orsino" 170
    "Pilot Us" 155
    "Seniceva" 150
    "Shung King" 58
    "Silver Bell" 163
    "Sir Fred Parkes" 170
    "Skomer" 119
    "Southern Cross" 162
    "St. Finbarr" 170
    "St. Giles" 156
    "Tarrad" 146
    "Tirpitz" 112, 117
    "Titanic" 27
    "Venus" 163
    "Victor Allcard" 153
    "Vineyard" 26
    "Western Belle" 146
    "William Taylor Of Oldham" 131
    "Yin Hung" 58
Mark-ups 188
Maudslay 73, 89-90, 121
Maunsell Sea Fort 111
MCW 176, 190, 192 ,v
Mercedes 176, 196
Miesse 92
Ministry Of Supply 111, 121
Mirlees Blackstone 190
Mobil Economy Run 103, 160
Monte Carlo Rally 101

N

Neoplan 192
Norris & Henty Ltd. 17-18, 42
Norris, Henty & Gardners Ltd.
    42, 47, 64, 67, 78, 90, 95, 111,
    121, 124, 131, 133, 136-137,
    155, i
Northern General 192
Northern Motor Utilities 73

O

Orme, Stan, M.P. 179
Osborne, Samuel 136

P

Paccar 195
Pagefield 71, 74, 76, 81, 82, 86,
    96
Parkinson, Mr 71
Parkinson, T.H. 73
Peerless 74-75, 78, 89
Perkins 148, 162, 166, 193, 195
Petter 55, 190
Plane, Cyril 133, 136-137
Plane, Jack 136
Plaxton 192
Priestman 15

R

RAC 1000 Miles Rally 101
Ricardo Engineering Consultancy
    56-57, 69
Ricardo, Harry 55, 92
RNLI 131, 133, 151, 153-154,
    198
Robinson Hot Air Engine 11-12,
    14, 47
Robinson Patent Gas Engine 12
Robinson, A. E. & H. 11-13
Robinson, Horace 11
Rolls Royce 52, 55, 111, 164,
    171, 173, 175-176, 181, 183,
    188-189, 193, 195-196
Rover 52
Royal Navy 50
Ruston & Hornsby 52, 55, 183

S

Saurer 66
Sawyer, Capt. Tom 170
Scammell 78, 86-87, 89, 111,
    120, 137,144-145, 153, 161,
    165, 190, 192
Scania 176, 195-196
Screwbrie, Tom 187
Sebastian, Mr 164
Seddon Atkinson 190-192,
    194-195, 197, vi
Seddon Diesel Vehicles 138,
    161-162, 165, 171, 175, 189, ii
Sheffield Corporation Transport
    74, 80
Shefflex 89
Smith, Harold 47
Smith, Jim 182, 187
Smiths of Rodley 90, 127, 166,
    168
Stagecoach UK 197
Stamper, G.A. 197, vi
Stephenson, George and Robert
    6
Stothert & Pitt 82
Stott, Connie and Maude 7
Straker Squire 76
Sunbeam 52
Sutton, Alf (Sutton & Sons)
    171-172

T

Tasmanian Railways 125
Texas Group 195-196
Thatcher, Margaret, M.P. 191
Thompstone, Gordon 133, 158,
    179, 181
Thornycroft, J.I. 69
Thornycroft of Basingstoke, 90,
    137, iii

Tilling-Stevens 72, 74-76, 78, 81,
    86, 90, 130, i
Todd, Eric 133, 158
Toft & Tomlinson 78
Tonanco reverse gear 196
Travancore Transport, iii
Trinity House 131, 150-151
Turner Transfer Co. 143-145
Twin-Disc reverse gear 180-181,
    196

V

Value of engines 201
Van de Steen, Mr 159
Vauxhall 52
Vickers 25, 50
Volvo 176, 195-196
Vulcan 86, 89-90, 96

W

Walker & Greig 56
Walker Bros. 71, 74-75, 81-82,
    93, 96, 104, 123-125
Wallis & Stevens 74
Walsall Corporation 78
War Office 25, 52
Warburg, S. G. & Co. Ltd. 184
Westfield Transport 144-145
White, iii
Whitworth, Sir Joseph 8
Wilkinson, Frank 7, 109, 121,
    158, 181
Wilkinson, T. 7
Wolseley, 52
Wynmalen & Hausmann 47

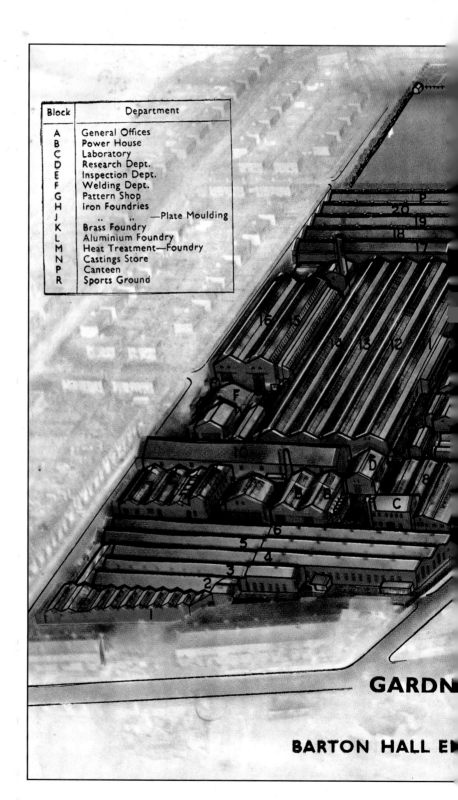

Block	Department
A	General Offices
B	Power House
C	Laboratory
D	Research Dept.
E	Inspection Dept.
F	Welding Dept.
G	Pattern Shop
H	Iron Foundries
J	,, ,, —Plate Moulding
K	Brass Foundry
L	Aluminium Foundry
M	Heat Treatment—Foundry
N	Castings Store
P	Canteen
R	Sports Ground

GARDN

BARTON HALL E